*This book is dedicated to life's journey
and the twist and turns it takes
to achieve its purpose and reveal the true
human spiritual experience.*

*To the sacrifices, compromises,
and losses that made my life come alive.*

LATOYA DIVINE

FAITH TO STRENGTH

The love she wanted,
the strength she received

BEAVER'S POND
PRESS

a novel

ISBN 13: 978-1-59298-804-4
Library of Congress Catalog Number: 2018911607
Printed in the United States of America
First Printing: 2019
23 22 21 20 19 5 4 3 2 1

Book design and typesetting by Dan Pitts.

Contact LaToya Divine at www.latoyadivine.com for speaking engagements, book club discussions, and interviews.

Beaver's Pond Press
7108 Ohms Lane
Edina, MN 55439–2129
BEAVER'S POND PRESS (952) 829-8818
www.BeaversPondPress.com

To order, visit www.ItascaBooks.com or email: orders@itascabooks.com.
Reseller discounts available.

CONTENTS

PROLOGUE
THE DAY HE DIDN'T OPEN THE DOOR

May 2015

I got in my car and entered the address into the GPS. It said it would take forty-five minutes to get there. All the way there, I thought about what I would say. Should I smile or keep a serious face? I didn't want to come across as lighthearted about the situation, because it couldn't be further from the truth. Still, I wanted to come across as friendly enough to break down the walls so we could at least say one word to each other.

I guess I'll figure it out when I get there, I said to myself.

"Make a right turn on Valley Creek Road," my friendly GPS told me. I made the turn. "Your destination will be on the left." I entered a housing community. "Arriving at your destination."

I pulled up to a small townhome. There wasn't a car in the driveway.

This was the home he had wanted to move our new family into.

I drove past the house to look for parking. The visitor lot was down the street. I avoided parking in the open and instead parked beside a black pickup truck so I couldn't be easily seen. It wasn't as though he knew what kind of car I drove, but I still wanted to be inconspicuous.

Okay, it was time. It had been at least four months since everything happened. I got out of my car and confidently walked toward the house, still wondering what my first words would be but knowing I had good intentions for having a civil conversation.

I rang the doorbell. No answer. I rang the doorbell again. No answer. I opened the screen door and knocked on the main door. No answer. He wasn't home. It was only four o'clock in the afternoon; he probably hadn't come home from work yet.

I walked back to my car. With my eyes fixed on the house, I reclined my seat a bit, tilted my head to the side, and waited for him to get home.

An hour passed, and he still wasn't home. I continued to lean back and wait. Then, in a blink of my eye, I saw a car move out of the driveway and head down the street. It was him! I looked back at the house, and the garage door was now open. Did the car come out of the garage? If so, did that mean he had been home when I rang the doorbell? Or did he just come home from work, then drive off again? How could I have totally missed that? Not knowing where the car had come from made such a difference.

Now what would I do? I had no intentions of driving back here again. The fact that I drove all this way here to see him was the last ounce of effort I was willing to put out. Plus, if he had known I was here today and had still refused to open the door, what would make him open the door some other time?

Well, I had to know for sure, so I decided to wait again. Two hours passed, and I had to use the bathroom. I was so thankful I had noticed a Starbucks in the area. Since I was officially on a stakeout, it was the closest restroom from my post. I hoped he wouldn't come back while I was away.

When I returned, I parked farther away this time to ensure I could get a wider look of the house and garage.

My cell phone rang.

"Hello," I answered.

"Hi, Justyne. It's Kelly. Just calling to see how you are doing." Kelly was one of our closest friends.

"I'm doing great," I replied in as normal a voice as I could manage. "Work is going well."

I couldn't tell her what I was really doing. Heck, I couldn't tell anyone what I was doing. I knew I had to follow this one out on my own.

"I listened to the lecture you sent me," Kelly said. "It was awesome. I loved the way the speaker spoke about dominion in marriage and the importance of the wife as a helpmate to the—"

"Ah . . . Kelly? Can I give you a call back? Something just came up, and I need to get to it."

I had to quickly rush Kelly off the phone. His car was pulling into the driveway. I hurried out of the car and ran to the house to catch him before he went inside, but the garage door was closing.

I knocked on the garage door. Nothing. I walked over to ring the doorbell. No answer. I knocked on the door. No answer. I decided to call his cell phone. No answer. I sent a text. No response.

I couldn't believe my husband was behaving this way. I walked back to the car, fuming. It had been almost four months. We hadn't spoken. We hadn't communicated. I thought things would have cooled down by now for us to have a mature and reasonable conversation. But clearly the answer was no.

I sat in the car for a few minutes more. I didn't want to give up too soon. I knew that if I left, I would never come back to the house again. I wanted to give it a chance.

I decided to walk back to the door. This time, I couldn't knock on the main door because he had locked the screen door. I couldn't believe he came out only to do that. I was shocked and furious. I shook my head in disappointment as I walked back to my car.

I called my husband's friend Peter, who had been his best man at our wedding.

"Hey, Peter. It's Justyne. I'm calling about something very specific. Have you spoken to John lately?" I wasted no time and got straight to the purpose of my call.

"Hey! Actually, I did a couple of days ago," Peter eagerly replied.

"Okay, because I'm outside his house in Seattle right now, and he's not answering the door. Does he know where I'm living now?" I asked.

"Uh, no. When I asked him, he said he didn't know where you were," Peter replied in surprise.

"Really. So for all he knows, I could be coming off a plane just to see him—and this is the way he behaves?" I started to get more upset.

"You know, I think he just needs some time," Peter advised.

"Oh, really?" I exclaimed. "So I shouldn't camp out in front of his house until morning, when he has no choice but to come outside?" I asked this jokingly but was seriously thinking about it.

"I think he just needs some time. He's really hurt and angry," Peter further explained.

"Hurt and angry about what?" Too many questions came to my mind. I shook my head again. "So should I just leave?"

"Yes. I would. But I don't want to tell you what to do." Peter tried to be diplomatic with his response.

"Okay."

I accepted what Peter said. I turned on the car and prepared for my journey back home.

At the very least, I had expected my husband to open the door, even if only to say, "I don't want to talk to you." He didn't know if I had come off a plane. He didn't know how far I had traveled to see him. He didn't care where I was living. He didn't want to hear what I had to say. He didn't answer the door.

The next day, I received a call from my mother.

"Hey, Justyne. How are you doing? I received two messages from John's mom saying I need to call her. Do you know why she would be calling?" my mom sincerely asked.

"No. You should call her back."

I didn't tell my mom what had happened. Instead, I waited to hear what she had to say after she'd had a chance to speak with John's mom.

Within two hours, Mom called back.

"Hi, again. I missed talking to you yesterday. How was your day?"

Mom was starting the conversation slowly with small talk.

"I'm fine. What did his mother say? Why did she call?" I was eager to find out about the conversation.

"Did you go over to see John yesterday?" Mom directly asked.

"Yes, but—" I didn't have a chance to explain before my mother interrupted.

"Why would you do that? He called his mom and said you went over there to harass him. You see, the boy is no good."

Once my mom started, she didn't stop. She was just as upset as I was about the situation. I was the youngest of two children and the only girl, so my mother took everything that happened to me personally. She guarded me with fierce pride.

Then my dad picked up the other phone to join the conversation. My parents said it was clear John had no intentions of resolving the relationship and that he was trying to paint a bad picture of me.

I listened and listened, then came to the realization that the situation with John had reached a new level of ignorance and immaturity. It wasn't even worth thinking or talking about anymore. Perhaps I shouldn't have shown up at his home unannounced, but I was still his wife. John had reached a low that truly disgusted me.

But instead of getting more upset, I decided to let it go. The following day, I sent John an email.

Subject: I apologize . . .

Hi, John-
I'm sorry that my showing up at your home upset and offended you in any way. My intention was to positively open the lines of communication.

You take care!
Justyne

PART I

THE BEGINNING TO THE END

1

WHEN WE FIRST MET

March 2008

As an undergrad in college, I was a member of a student organization that promoted skill development and careers in engineering and technology. Because I was in the information technology program, I joined the organization to gain more insight into career opportunities in my field and to meet other diverse students. Together, we traveled to different schools, facilitated workshops, attended conferences, and shared life together for at least four years. It was one of the best experiences of my college career, so when I graduated and started working in my field, I decided to still be part of the organization through volunteering.

Our organization held a national convention each year. I was part of the planning team for the 2009 national convention in Montreal. My hometown was Belleville, Ontario, a small town a few hours from Montreal. So in March 2008, I attended the convention in Las Vegas to shadow the current program director, as I was scheduled to serve that role the following year. Over the three-day conference, my agenda was packed with meetings and shadowing activities to learn as much as possible. Being program director involved knowing all the different workshops taking place throughout the conference in all streams: high school, college, and postgraduate.

The trip to Las Vegas came at a good time to get my mind off things. I had just broken up with Michael Turner. Well, it was much more than a breakup; we had ended our engagement. However, Michael had registered for the conference too. Michael studied computer engineering, but we hadn't attended the same school. I expected him to be there at the conference, but I wasn't sure if I would see him.

Day two of the convention was hectic with behind-the-scenes activities. I was putting program booklets together when I looked up and saw Michael from a distance walking through the conference hall. I dropped what I was doing and started to walk in his direction. But he was walking too fast—I couldn't keep up with him in the crowded hall. I eventually stopped and watched Michael turn the corner. I hoped I would see him again.

Later that day, I decided to take a walk through the career fair to see what companies were represented. I stopped at the Google booth to talk to representatives. As I was talking to the recruiter, I noticed a tall, husky guy at the next booth. He was looking at the materials on his table, but he looked up a few times in my direction—enough times until we made eye contact.

When I finished my conversation with the Google rep, I headed in the other direction to another booth. Then I heard a voice.

"Hey! You're not going to check out our booth?" the voice called out to me.

I turned around and saw it was the tall, husky guy I'd just seen moments before.

"Oh, I was just walking around," I replied as I headed back to him.

"So are you part of the organization?" he asked, noticing my conference planner T-shirt.

"Yeah! I'm on next year's conference planning team," I proudly replied.

We continued the back-and-forth casual conversation for minutes until I got his name. *John Black.* John was big and muscular like a football player and carried himself with a professional demeanor. I enjoyed our conversation. Unlike most guys, he didn't come across as aggressive, as if he were trying to pick me up. By the end of the conversation, we exchanged Facebook contacts and said we'd stay in touch. I set off to continue viewing other booths.

After visiting most of the booths upstairs, I jumped on the escalators to head back downstairs to the conference planning committee meeting I was almost late for. When I stepped off the escalator, my eyes met with Michael's. He seemed happy to see me, and I was happy to see him.

"Hey! What's up? You're here!" Michael quickly said, then he leaned in to give me a hug.

It was awkward. Neither of us quite knew how to greet the other, and it was clear we each had places we needed to be.

"Yeah, I got here yesterday. What about you?" I replied.

"Me too. I mean, I got here yesterday too. I'm on my way to a workshop right now. What are you doing later?" Michael asked.

"I'm on my way to a meeting now, but I have nothing planned for this evening."

"Do you want to meet up later to catch up?"

"Yeah, that would be okay."

We planned to meet at the Bellagio fountain at seven o'clock that night. When we went our separate ways, I had the biggest smile on my face.

Michael and I had known each other since we were eight years old and probably even before then because our parents had been friends since the early '70s. We used to play with action figures and dolls as kids, but then we didn't see each other for a few years.

I remember the day when we saw each other again. We were about fourteen years old. Michael and his mom came to visit my parents at our house. My brother was in the basement playing video games, and I was upstairs in my room. My mom called me downstairs to say hello to Michael's mom.

"Oh my God. Is this little Justyne? Oh my! She has grown up so nicely. Turn around and let me see you!"

Ms. Turner was smiling from ear to ear. I smiled as well to be nice. But it was one of those moments every teenager has experienced—when you wish you could disappear.

"Michael is downstairs," my mom told me.

"Do you remember Michael?" Ms. Turner asked.

"Yes. I remember the birthday party and the pool at your house," I replied.

"Oh yes! You have a good memory. That's right. That's when we lived on Flower Street." Ms. Turner was so happy we shared a memory.

I proceed downstairs to see what my brother and Michael were up to. When I got to the bottom of the stairs and saw Michael, he just stared at me. He looked mesmerized. He looked at me as if I had come out of the sky. I felt so special and pretty in that moment.

"Hi." I looked at Michael looking at me.

"Hi," Michael said with a smile. "So, yeah—I remember you. What school do you go to?"

"I go to Saint Catherine High School," I replied.

I took a seat on a chair beside my brother and Michael to watch them play *Street Fighter* on the computer. I didn't stay too long, as I could see my brother wanted to get back into the video game without the distraction of my presence.

As I started back upstairs, I overheard Michael say to my brother, "That's your *sister*, guy?"

I smiled. But I never knew that moment would change my life forever.

Michael and I began the kind of teenage romance people dream about. We would stay on the phone for hours, until the sun came up the next day. We'd talk about nothing and everything at the same time. He always made time for me. Always.

Five months into our relationship, we got into a silly argument. I was mad at him because he had gotten me flowers but then had thrown them at me rather than hand them to me nicely. Maybe he threw them because he was upset about something I did. Or maybe he didn't technically throw them at all—maybe I just didn't like the way he gave me the flowers. Whatever it was, we got mad at each other while at his house, and I ended up leaving and going home.

That night, I was volunteering at the city hospital in the pediatric ward. I was sixteen, with hopes of becoming of a pediatrician, so I decided to get some early experience by volunteering at the hospital on Monday and Wednesday nights.

I was in the children's playroom when I heard a voice say, "Hello . . ."

I turned around and saw Michael in his brown leather jacket, carrying a new bouquet of flowers and his big smile. I gave him the biggest hug and kissed him on the lips. I felt special. I knew he loved me.

Looking back at our relationship over the years, I realized that I took what we had for granted and made a mess out of everything. We constantly went back and forth in our relationship because I didn't take him seriously most times.

After a year into our teenage relationship, I stopped talking to Michael to date another guy I had liked since second grade. According to Michael, I cheated on him, because he claimed I hadn't clarified to him that we weren't dating anymore. Nothing formal had been said. I just stopped calling, and he didn't call either. Everything stopped without a word said.

I eventually went back to where my heart was, with Michael. But I knew things weren't the same. Even his mom said to him, "Don't take her back if she left you to date someone else." I knew Michael was hurt and didn't look at me the same, and that completely devastated me. But I didn't know we would spend the next fifteen years of our lives repairing our deep feelings for each other and trying to get back to the place where we had been at sixteen years old.

Michael and I went through many breakups and makeups, but one thing I knew for sure was that I wanted to spend my life with him. I wanted to share this life with him. I knew he wanted the same thing too. But Michael was a huge procrastinator, always trying to figure out something that was already right in front of him.

So, many years and a broken engagement later, I got dressed to meet Michael at the Bellagio fountain at seven o'clock.

We met at the center point of the fountain and decided to go out to dinner at one of the hotel restaurants on the strip. Sitting across from Michael after our breakup was a bit uncomfortable. I was still upset. But Michael didn't take me seriously. He just laughed because he knew my heart and knew I couldn't be that upset with him. He knew I was just putting up a fake tough wall.

After dinner, we spent the rest of the night walking the strip, going in and out of casinos, then we went back to his hotel. We ordered hot chocolate, my favorite, and a few snacks. We spent the night in each other's arms, rekindling the genuine love between us.

While at the convention the next morning, I called Michael and also sent a text message, letting him know I was leaving Las Vegas later that afternoon. I said I would call him when I got home.

I received a simple text message back:

Okay.

When I got home, I noticed my additional text messages and calls were not returned. Then I checked my email and saw I had a message from Michael.

Subject: Hi

I think our time in Las Vegas was special, but we should leave it as that. I don't think we should get back together.

Michael

I stared at the email and reread it over and over again. I was shocked and hurt. I thought of the worst thing I could possibly write back, and I did just that. I vowed to never talk to Michael ever again.

A month after that episode, I was on Facebook one night and got a message from John Black. He was checking up on me to see how I was doing. I replied in the same casual way he sent his message. We both ended by saying good-night and signing off. It was just what I needed at that time.

2

THE DAY I GAVE HIM THE PAPERS

December 2015

I returned home to Houston on December 27 after spending Christmas away from John. Before I left, I had taken off my engagement ring and wedding band and put them in the bottom of my jewelry box as well as printed out some divorce papers I'd found online. I filled out the information, signed the papers, and put them in my bag. I didn't know when I would give them to John, but I knew the time would come soon.

The night I returned home, John refused to let me sleep in our bed. He spread himself across our king-size bed, preventing me from getting in.

It was the last trigger. I went straight to my bag, pulled out the divorce papers, and gave them to John. All they needed was his signature. The time was now.

I had contemplated divorce before. I had let him know it was the direction we were heading if things didn't change. Our three-year marriage had been challenging since day one, more than I thought it should be. But John ignorantly considered any talk of divorce as a threat rather than a serious wakeup call to address issues.

When I handed John the papers, he threw them back at me. "Those don't belong in here!"

I didn't know what "here" meant. On our bed? In the bedroom? In our marriage? I didn't know. What I did know was that he felt I didn't belong in the bedroom.

I gathered my pillows and blanket to exit. After my last step out of the room, I heard John shut and lock the bedroom door.

I headed to the couch in the living room, which was just one room over. There I would spend the first of many nights. I spread the blanket across the couch, tucking in the crease to get it tight, and propped the pillows at the end. I lay down, spread the blanket over myself, and just closed my eyes.

The next few days, John and I passed each other as if we didn't exist. He didn't speak to me, and I didn't speak to him. He didn't bring up the divorce papers, and I didn't ask. Each night, I took a shower in the bathroom in our bedroom, then gathered my blanket and pillow and went to the couch. And each night, I heard the door close behind me, with the violent force of the lock being turned to ensure I didn't come back in.

It was now December 30, and I started to think about how I would spend New Year's Eve. I knew I didn't want to spend New Year's with someone who was ignoring me, but I wasn't sure what I would do instead.

That night while I was sitting on the couch watching TV, John walked past me. But before going into the bedroom, he turned to me.

"Where are those divorce papers you want me to sign?" he asked.

"I have them. Do you want them now?" I replied.

"You can give them to me tomorrow."

"Okay."

John went into the bedroom and once again locked the door.

Soon after, I contacted my friend Susan. I had spent Christmas with her and her family in nearby Pasadena, and now I let her know I'd be coming back to spend New Year's as well.

When I returned after the visit with Susan, days and nights went by without a single communication and with me still sleeping on the couch. Each night, I plugged in my earphones to watch YouTube videos on my phone until I fell asleep. I had to remain quiet because John's sister Blossom was sleeping upstairs. Blossom had come from the Cayman Islands about two years earlier to help us out with the restaurant.

The restaurant was something John had wanted to open, and I had been happy to help him do it as a supportive wife. While we were in the process of signing the contracts for the restaurant, John had to start traveling for his job. It made sense, then, that I would help get the restaurant up and running.

I had planned it to be a career shift, actually. I had just been let go from my job. But even before I was let go, I had wanted to stop traveling so I could be closer to home and be more stable to raise our future family. I was excited for the opportunity to work in the restaurant business and possibly focus on event planning and management as a new career. The sky was the limit, and I was ready to take hold of all the opportunities presented to us.

When the restaurant was approaching its grand opening, John decided to bring in Blossom to help. I hesitated about the idea. I didn't fully understand her role or how long she would be staying. John told me a few times that she would stay in the States only a few months. She'd stay with us at first, then she'd get her own car and place. Really? Why would she need a car and a place if she were just staying a few months? Blossom was married herself with children. Where was her family?

Anyway, I rolled with it . . . and rolled with it . . . until a few months became almost two years of her living with us. Blossom was constantly on the phone. I was convinced the phone was part of her ear. I had to use earphones while on my own couch to drown out the loud chatter coming from upstairs.

John still had the divorce papers but didn't say anything about them. It was now two weeks into the new year, and nothing had been said, so I decided to ask him on a Saturday afternoon.

"Hey, John, are you going to give me back the divorce papers?"

"Yes. I'm still reviewing them. I'll give them back to you soon," he replied sternly.

"Okay," I said.

Another week passed, and John kept silent. While at the restaurant one day, I found John in the office.

"Last week you said you were reviewing the divorce papers, but you didn't say when you'd give them back."

I was tired of not knowing what was going on. I just wanted an answer, a conversation, something.

"When I am ready, I will give them to you. Now leave." John barely restrained his anger as he snapped at me and firmly put his hand on the desk.

Later that day, when John, Blossom, and I returned home, John handed me the signed divorce papers in our bedroom as he was packing to go back out of town for work. His current project was in Seattle, which required John to travel and be away from home for weeks at a time.

My first reaction was relief. Finally, it was clear he wanted the divorce too. For the first time during our marriage, I had direction. But the signed papers were just the beginning. I took the papers from him and instantly started thinking about next steps.

"Okay. Thanks. There are other documents to fill out as well. I'll email those to you."

"That's fine," John replied as he walked out of the bedroom.

After John left, I spent the evening preparing the rest of the documents to send him. Before going to bed, I received a phone call from Peter. He quickly fit in all he wanted say in three sentences.

"Hey, Justyne—I just talked to John. I know he gave you back the divorce papers signed, but throw them away, okay? My wife and I will set up a mediation with you guys to talk this out."

"Okay," I replied. That was all I could say.

I'd always been open to talking this out, but I didn't have anyone to talk to about it, and John wasn't a person I could resolve anything with on my own.

Soon after, I received a text message from John.

> Peter would like you to rip up
> the divorce papers on his behalf.

In other words, John had to make sure I knew I should destroy the divorce papers not because he wanted me to but because his friend wanted me to. I replied to the text, then I went to bed.

> Okay. Thanks for letting me know.

The following day, I received a text from Peter letting me know we'd have a conference call at eight o'clock that evening.

The restaurant was closed, so I spent the day in the bedroom, awaiting the conversation that night. When it was almost eight o'clock, I logged in to the conference line Peter had set up. We were able to see each other online as well with the video feature.

Peter and his wife spent the first couple of minutes sharing their marriage experience and journey to offer us support for the challenges we were going through. Peter asked which one of us wanted to speak first.

"She can go first. Let her talk," John said in a cold and arrogant tone.

"Okay, Justyne," Peter said.

But I didn't even get a chance to speak because John decided he had something to say first after all.

"Before she starts, I just want to let you know the only reason I signed the divorce papers was to show I was in agreement with it, because I was so fed up with the whole situation."

Well, I thought, *isn't that why people sign divorce papers—because they both agree with that direction?* I wasn't sure what was behind John's statement. And I hated how he referred to me as "she" and not by my name.

Now that I finally had my chance to talk, I started to express what I thought were the top three problems in our marriage.

"The first problem is the unanswered questions with no honest and truthful responses. Like, where did you get the bike? When are we moving to Seattle? How long is your sister staying with us, and what's the future plan? The second thing is the dismissal of my feelings and concerns—"

"Wait," John interrupted. "I spoke to you about my sister. She isn't the problem."

"Hey, John, your wife was speaking, and you interrupted her. The purpose of this is to listen to each other," Peter chimed in to bring the discussion back to focus.

"Well, she's not saying anything that has to do with the problem."

It didn't take long for John to jump in to deflect and defend himself. I never got the chance to finish expressing my top three problems before the conversation escalated to the point of John screaming "*Shut up!*" at me.

"Hey, man, look at how you're talking to your wife," Peter said in disbelief. I think he was just beginning to realize how little he knew about his friend.

"I know, but you don't understand. I'm really upset right now. I . . ." John started to explain himself but couldn't finish.

It was clear John wasn't ready to accept that some of his decisions had not been in the best interest of his marriage and wife. Nor could he accept that the more he continued to be in denial and not talk to me about things that affected both of our lives, the more he would lose me.

John logged off the conference line before we finished the meditation session. That left just me, Peter, and his wife on the call.

Peter expressed his final thoughts: "If neither of you want this marriage, then fine. But *someone* has to want this marriage if it's going to have a chance."

I knew Peter was right. I knew that "someone" who could get our marriage to the point of having a chance would have to be me. But I wasn't there. I had reached the point where I truly didn't want to be married to John. He wasn't a man I wanted to be with. John lacked the emotional maturity to express any type of emotion that wasn't defensive, and he wasn't able to face issues and participate on the path to reconciliation. The issue that was pulling us apart was the issue I was living in, and John refused to do anything about it.

Soon after the explosive conference call, I started to think about the things I needed in place if I ended up leaving for good. I thought about the accounts, especially the savings account.

There was some money in the account, but not much. Within a year, it had gone from $10,000 to barely $3,000. John wasn't consistently putting money into the main account to cover the bills, and I wasn't working. When I had been working, though, I put money into it. And at this point, it was all the money I had.

I asked John if he would deposit any money into the main account to cover the bills for the month. He said no. Well, I would no longer transfer money from the savings into the checking account to cover the bills he refused to help pay.

I told John I would close the accounts. I even sent him an email listing all the bills that were due and when he would need to make arrangements to cover them. Then I closed both checking and savings accounts and held on to the remaining money. I didn't want to give John anything out of it, seeing as he had made me sign a postnuptial agreement just a few months before. So I kept the money, hoping he would forget and not ask me about it.

I forwarded my mail to my parents' home in Belleville so I wouldn't have important documents coming to the house in Houston anymore. I had to feel as though I had a plan, even though I didn't have one. All I knew in the moment was that I had to start protecting myself.

John eventually asked about the remaining balance in the bank accounts.

"Did you close the savings account?"

"Yes."

"Where is the money?"

"I have it. I'm going to hang on to it. If anything happens, you'll leave me with nothing." I didn't hold back what I thought and how I felt.

"No, that's not true. But I need half of the money today," John unsympathetically replied.

"Well, I won't be able to do that," I firmly replied.

It took me a moment to realize John's audacity to ask for half the money from the savings account that was in my name, when he had initiated a postnuptial agreement to prevent me from claiming anything we had shared together during our marriage.

Eventually, though, my good conscience got the best of me. I deposited $1,000 into John's account later that week. I thought it was the right thing to do, even though I really didn't want to. Later, however, I would realize how naively innocent it was of me. John would end up owing me a lot more.

The silence between John and me grew stronger and more intense. Each weekend John came home, it was a surprise to me. He didn't tell me when he was coming. Instead, he told his sister. He didn't have any reason to talk to me about the restaurant. Instead, he'd call his sister. He didn't have to ask me anything about the house. Instead, he'd call his sister. Everything was funneled through his sister and then to me. John sought resolution in her.

There was no reason for me to stay any longer.

In one final attempt, I asked John during an argument in the bedroom, "Are you willing to go to counseling?"

"*Yes!*" he screamed.

"Okay. I'll schedule an appointment." I left the bedroom and returned to the couch.

I scheduled the initial appointment with the counselor, but John had to join by Skype because he wasn't in town. I didn't like that John hadn't even made time to attend the appointment in person. I wasn't sure whether he had agreed to counseling because he truly wanted it to help us or because he just wanted to say he had "participated" in something.

During the appointment, the counselor asked John general questions to get to know him. I remained quiet. At the end of the appointment, the counselor made it very clear to John that if he wanted his marriage, he would need to make time to be here in person for the sessions.

It was Sunday, February 1. I was at the house alone, getting ready to wash my hair. I sent John an email.

> **Subject: Follow-up and next steps**
>
> It's been about two weeks since the appointment with the counselor . . . I would like to know if you intend to make time to participate in counseling.

John emailed back.

> **Subject: Re: Follow-up and next steps**
>
> Go ahead and schedule it for tomorrow.

What? Tomorrow? Not only did John not tell me he would be in town tomorrow, but he decided to tell me on Sunday to schedule an appointment for Monday. What if I hadn't sent him the email to ask?

Fortunately, I was able to schedule an appointment. I emailed John to let him know.

> **Subject: Re: Follow-up and next steps**
>
> The appointment is scheduled for 2:00 p.m. tomorrow.

John didn't reply. I continued washing my hair.

3

WHEN WE RECONNECTED

August 2010

Two years had passed since the convention in Vegas. I had reached a point of peace in my life. I was doing things on my own again and hanging out with friends. I was over Michael Turner and was ready for the next chapter of my life. I was looking forward to the future. I wasn't anxious—I was open for anything that came my way. I was happy just working and spending days at home watching movies.

That's when I heard from John again on Facebook. He sent me a message to let me know he would be coming to Montreal, near my hometown, that summer.

> Hi, Justyne—
> How have you been? I hope you remember me from the conference in Las Vegas a couple of years ago. I hope everything has been going well for you. I want to let you know I'll be in your neck of the woods in the a few months to attend the Montreal jazz festival. I've heard so much about it, and it will be my first time attending, so I'm looking forward to it. I'm starting to plan my trip and the activities to check out. If you have any suggestions, please let

> me know. I hope to reconnect with you in Montreal.
> See you soon!
> Take care,
> John

I replied.

> Hey, John!
> Nice to hear from you! All is good. Great to hear you'll be in Montreal this year. I haven't heard about the must-go parties yet, but I'll definitely let you know when I start hearing the buzz, and I will also send you a few links. Please let me know how your plans shape up so we can connect while you're here.
> Take care,
> Justyne

It was Thursday, August 5, and the city of Montreal was getting ready for the big jazz festival that attracted many tourists. John had arrived and was in the city. I was working downtown that day, so I let him know I could meet up over my lunch hour.

I walked a few blocks from my office and looked for the dark-gray car John told me he and his friend Sam were driving. I spotted the car and jumped in the back seat before the cars behind us started coming down the street after the red light changed.

I leaned over to greet John and Sam but couldn't see John very well. I then realized I had forgotten what he even looked like.

We took a driving tour of the city, which took more time than we'd realized because of traffic. At last, we stopped at the popular mall downtown. When we got out of the car, I finally got a better look at John. I noticed his tall, husky, muscular frame and knocked knees.

It was cute. I didn't stare for too long but thought he was a good-looking guy. He looked like a guy who had a lot of girls chasing him. It was just an observation, but I didn't know for sure.

"So where will you guys go for lunch?" I asked.

"Not sure—hey, wait. You're not coming with us?" John asked, surprised.

"No, sorry. I can't. I have to get back to work," I replied apologetically. "My lunchtime is over."

I let the guys know where to go for lunch, then jumped on the bus to go back to the office.

That evening and the next, John texted me about joining them for dinner. But each time, I passed. The first night, I was tired and already on my way home. The next time, I decided to stay in. I had become such a homebody. Although it was festival weekend, I wasn't up to going to any parties.

The day of the festival, though, I let John know I would be downtown that evening so we could meet up. Every year, I took my parents downtown to the Harbourfront to enjoy the live entertainment, so that's where I headed for the evening with my parents. John sent a text to let me know he was close by. He was getting ready to board a party boat. But by the time I saw the message, he had already boarded, and we missed each other again.

It was Sunday. I had just gotten home from church, and I felt bad I hadn't spent time with John during his visit. So I told myself I would go out today. I sent John a text to find out what he was up to. Based on his reply, I think John wondered if I were a hermit:

> Oh, so you're coming out of hiding today?

I smiled at the slight jab, then replied to let him know I would meet him and Sam at the mall near where they were staying.

I had worn a long black sundress to church, and I just put a jean jacket over it. I drove about twenty minutes to the mall. It was a beautiful day, and I thought about where I could take John to enjoy the city. I sat in front of one of the department stores and waited for John and his friend to arrive. Ten minutes passed, then I looked up to see John and Sam walking toward me. I noticed John lean in to Sam to say something with a grin on his face. I could tell it was something pleasant. I think he liked what he saw.

"Have you been waiting long?" John asked as he gave me a hug.

"No, not too long," I replied as I finished greeting him and Sam.

"So where do you want to go?" John didn't waste any time.

"I was thinking of the music fest at the city park," I suggested.

"That sounds good. We also want to get some souvenirs before we leave tomorrow," John added.

"Oh, okay. So let's go downtown to a few souvenir shops, then we can go to the music fest from there," I concluded.

We were all set with a plan for the day. Before we headed downtown, I quickly followed them in my car back to the house where they were staying. I parked my car so we'd have only one vehicle, to keep things simple. As we headed downtown, I sat in the back seat to enjoy the ride. We talked back and forth as if we had been friends for years.

After an hour visiting souvenir shops, our next stop was the music fest. The park was crowded with tons of people and families enjoying the live music. Vendor booths surrounded the park. John pulled out a blanket for us to sit on. I was quite impressed that he had thought to grab a blanket while I parked my car at the house. He had also packed a couple of waters and drinks. The blanket was only big enough for two, so John and I sat while Sam walked around. I think Sam sensed that John wanted to be alone with me anyway.

"So, how old are you?" John innocently asked.

"Um, hmm . . . how old do I look?" I playfully replied.

"Oh no—I don't want to do that. That never goes well," John said hesitantly.

I laughed. "No, guess. I promise I won't get offended."

"Uh, okay . . . Twenty-six years old?" John reluctantly offered.

He guessed pretty well. It was five years younger than I really was, but I got that a lot. People always thought I looked younger.

"I'm thirty-one, turning thirty-two," I told him.

"Whoa!" we both chimed at the same time.

He didn't believe it. I could tell by the look on his face he was delighted.

"I just turned thirty-one myself," he said.

We spent the rest of the time talking about work, hobbies, and things we enjoyed doing.

"Do you see yourself married?" he asked at one point.

"Uh, yeah. I can see myself doing that," I casually replied. I'd learned not to focus on marriage too much due to my experience with Michael.

"Oh, okay. That's nice to know," John replied with a smile.

We continued talking about marriage and children. It was a good conversation. By the time Sam came back around, I had formed the impression that John was a really nice guy.

We ended up stopping for pizza after the music fest, then we made plans to go to a party downtown. It was an older crowd playing mature music—mostly old-school. We had a great time.

It was about one o'clock in the morning when we headed back to the house so I could get my car.

"It was nice seeing you again," Sam said. "Thank you for a great day and night. You did good!"

He gave me a hug and went into the house, leaving John and me alone outside standing by my car.

"Thanks for coming out today. I had a really great time. When will I see you again?" John didn't procrastinate.

I didn't know how to respond. I was so complacent in my life that I didn't even know how to tell if someone really liked me. It had been a while since I had been interested in anyone.

"I don't know. We'll see," I quickly replied.

John leaned in to give me a hug. I reciprocated, then got into my car. When I got home, I sent John a text to let him know I'd gotten home safely.

I went to sleep that night feeling good about the evening. I was happy to know I had met someone who made me smile.

When John got back home to Houston, Texas, he gave me a call. I was somewhat surprised to hear from him, but somewhat not surprised at the same time. I approached the potential new development in a very casual and friendly way.

It was the first of many phone conversations we had throughout the month. It became clear that John was interested in me, and I was interested in him. Over the next four months, we talked, texted, and even visited each other. By December, we'd set our wedding date for the following year.

4

THE DAY I LEFT

February 2015

February 2 started off as a normal day. I had gotten used to ignoring the dark clouds and awkward silence that surrounded the house. I got dressed for the counseling appointment and waited by the door for John to return from wherever he had gone early that morning.

John got home, passed me at the door, and went to the bedroom. He came back out, put his shoes back on, then headed for the door. I followed behind him.

We drove in silence, then at last John decided to say something.

"What do you hope to get out of the session?"

"Well, I hope to get clarity. I think we have different views of the situation and the problem, and we need to get some understanding about it," I replied.

"Oh. Okay." John's response was a bit distant, as if he didn't think the counseling session was necessary.

We got to the counselor's office and took a seat on the couch. The couch that solved all problems. The counselor gave each of us a piece of paper and pen so we could take notes. He started to explain the process of the sessions and what we could expect. He just kept talking and talking. I realized it was important for him to lay the foundation, but I also thought it was important that we, the clients, should talk and express our problem.

By the end of the session, we didn't get the chance to say much of anything. We left pretty much in the same state we came in.

Back in the car, I pulled the seat belt over me, then turned to John.

"Can we find a coffee shop so we can talk?" I asked. "I don't think we got the opportunity to express our points of view in the session."

"Oh, we don't need to go anywhere. We can talk here," John replied very harshly.

I didn't quite understand the hostility and hardness in his response. I didn't bother arguing with him, but my intention of going to a coffee shop had been to prevent us from arguing and yelling at each other.

"Okay," I obliged and continued. "We need to talk so we can figure out what we need to do. Obviously, I am not happy in this marriage. I don't think you participate in the marriage by acknowledging and addressing things—"

Then it happened, right on script. John interrupted me midsentence and argued with me about my own feelings.

It was over. I literally could not talk to someone who didn't listen and who constantly defended himself in such an ignorant way.

The drive home was beyond unpleasant. Because of John's inability to express his frustration, he grabbed my sunglasses in retaliation and threw them on the floor, ultimately shattering them. I started to call him every name in the book.

"I will need the credit cards for the restaurant," John suddenly demanded in the middle of our argument. John's priorities were clear, and reconciling our marriage wasn't one of them.

"I will give them to you later—when I am ready to give them to you," I replied. John had some nerve to ask for anything at this time.

We pulled into the driveway, and John parked in the garage. I didn't want to go inside and be trapped in the house with him and his sister. I needed space. I got out of the passenger's side and headed toward the driver's side.

"Where are you going?" John motioned for me to turn around and walk in front of him into the house.

"I'm going to IKEA to return something I bought," I replied, looking at him strangely.

"No, you're not. You are not driving this car."

"Why not? I put money in this car too."

"Well, you are not driving this car. Now *go*." John stood in front of me, pointing for me to go into the house, determined not to move until he saw me move.

I wasn't going to back down either. There was no way I would let him get away treating me like this.

I stood in place in the garage, contemplating my next move. John stood just a few feet away from me, blocking the garage door exit. The door to enter the house, where I could hear his sister in the kitchen, was behind me. I decided to open the passenger door to sit down and start my protest.

Within moments of taking a few deep breaths, John leaped before me and grabbed my handbag, thrusting me out of the car. He flipped my handbag over and dumped everything out of it. He then went for my wallet and started ripping things out.

I jumped on him to get him to stop, but he pushed me, and I fell down. I got back up and went after him. I started grabbing and kicking and punching him in his face until he dropped my stuff.

"*I hate you!*" I yelled out with tears down my face, still battling with him.

"Blossom! Blossom!" John called out for his sister. "Come here— look what Justyne is doing!"

Blossom came rushing into the garage. She pulled us apart, but I wanted to get at her too.

I picked up my handbag and laptop bag, then began gathering up my things from the garage floor. Within seconds, John leaped at me to grab the laptop bag. It was the laptop I used to manage everything at the restaurant. In a last desperate attempt, John tried to grab it away from me. I held on really strong to the bag until he eventually let it go.

"You are a boy! A pathetic boy!" Those were the only words that could come out of my mouth. I had no other words to describe how I saw John in that moment. I was disgusted.

John stormed inside the house but returned soon after. "Look what you did—you scratched me." He pointed to his face.

"Oh, please! Go put a Band-Aid on it—you boy!" I shouted back.

It was time to leave. It was beyond over. It was long overdue. I went inside and started packing every single thing I had in the house.

A week prior, I had gotten some boxes in preparation for this moment, though I had hoped I wouldn't have to use them. I had stored the boxes in the closet behind my clothes. As I was now gathering my things, John huffed into the bedroom. He looked around, watching me pack. He was even so "helpful" as to hand me items so I wouldn't forget anything.

"And make sure you get those boxes out of here!" he barked.

Yeah, I'm going to use those boxes to get the hell out of here, I thought.

I looked for my phone, but it was nowhere to be found.

"Do you have my phone?" I asked.

He didn't respond.

"I said, do you have my phone?"

He completely ignored me, leaving the room.

He was holding my phone hostage. I kept on packing. Then I remembered my tablet. I sent a quick email to my neighbor Cherie to come help me. I also had an internet phone, but her and everyone else's phone number was in my regular phone. I searched my emails to hopefully find her number. No luck. So I continued to pack, hoping she got my email.

After a while, I had to sit on the ottoman in the bedroom. I had to catch my breath. I realized I hadn't eaten anything all day. Packing was taking a lot more out of me than I expected. The emotions of the day were settling in as I felt the reality of the moment. I wanted to cry but couldn't.

Just then, John came back inside the room. "Hurry up. And you better get those boxes out of here."

"I need a break," I said as I took a sip from my water bottle.

"Well, that's too bad. You better hurry up," my husband replied.

I flung my hand as if shooing away a fly so he would leave the room.

Minutes later, I heard him watching television in the living room as Blossom made him dinner. He was laughing at whatever he was watching, as if my packing up all my belongings didn't mean anything to him.

"Come, John—eat. Dinner is ready," Blossom bellowed from the kitchen.

"Oh, I'm coming," John cheerfully said.

I still hadn't heard from Cherie. I did another search on Cherie's name in my tablet and finally found her phone number.

"Cherie, did you get my email?" I quickly said when she answered the phone.

"No. Why? What happened?" Cherie replied in anticipation.

"I need you to come over to help me move my things out. Things are not good. It got physical between John and me. I need to leave," I said as calmly as I could in an effort to manage her reaction. It didn't work.

"*Are you kidding me?* I can't believe this! I am so disappointed in John. I'm coming over right now!" Cherie hung up.

I next found the number for Kathy and her husband, Ken. They were longtime friends of John's and elders in the church we attended. I asked them to come to the house too. I hoped they would be able to reason with John so he could see his behavior.

I was sitting on the bed with my internet phone in my hands, leaning over and catching another breath, when John came back in the room with a mop and bucket to start cleaning the bedroom floor.

"I think it would be better for you to wait until I moved the boxes out," I said, watching John mop around my belongings.

"Well, you need to hurry up," John said in frustration, not wanting to admit that my idea made better sense. He finally rested the mop against the wall and walked out of the bedroom.

Knowing Cherie was on her way, I started to bring my boxes to the front door. I passed John and Blossom on the couch watching television. No one said a word. I continued going in and out of the bedroom, bringing more things out.

I opened the front door just as Cherie was walking up. I could see the anger on her face. She had known John for quite some time, when they moved into their homes at the same time. Although they were friends, there was still so much Cherie didn't know about John. She immediately picked up a box to bring out to her car. She didn't say anything to John and Blossom.

A few minutes later, Kathy and Ken arrived.

"Hey, man, what's going on?" Ken took a seat on the couch beside John.

John didn't say anything.

He didn't have anything to say. He wouldn't talk. I think it was too much for him to deal with. Now other people were witnessing his behavior, and he didn't like that at all. John was such a private person, and this situation embarrassed him.

I continued to bring things out of the house while Ken tried to engage John. I eventually stopped to join the conversation. Blossom sat there on the couch in the middle of it all until Cherie called her to go outside. Blossom clearly lacked the sense to know when to excuse herself from a situation that was none of her business.

"I think you guys need to 'date' to get to know each other all over again," Ken pleaded. "Don't pursue divorce right now. Just give it some time."

Ken and Kathy started to share about their marriage journey and the difficult times they went through. They hoped to encourage us. They didn't know John could be this stubborn to even allow that to penetrate.

Cherie and Blossom came back inside just in time for Ken to ask Blossom what she thought.

"Oh, I know, I know. I heard I'm the problem," she flagrantly started. "But I just put a Band-Aid over it." Blossom folded her legs and leaned back on the couch, clearly oblivious to the damage her presence and ignorance had caused.

Kathy turned to me. "What do you want, Justyne?"

The emotions and tears started to flow as I silently remembered the complete imbalance—I had sacrificed and compromised everything in the marriage while John had sacrificed and compromised nothing. I remembered all the times we didn't spend together and how it didn't matter to John. I remembered how he put his sister above his marriage and his wife, regardless of how many times I pleaded with him.

"I feel like I'm willing to work it out," I finally said, "but only with someone who is willing to work it out with me. John's attitude is like it's just me who needs to make all the changes in order for things to work. I've done wrong, yes, but so has he. Why can't he recognize that and come together to fix it? But he doesn't see that." At no time did I feel he cared about the marriage or wanted to rescue it.

John said nothing.

The tears rolled down my face. Those were some of the last words I said in that house.

All my things were packed up. I was ready to go. I asked John for my phone.

"I need the keys to the house, the car, and the restaurant, and I need the business credit cards and health card first," John replied.

I gathered those things for him and placed them on the kitchen counter. John went into the garage, pretending my phone was in there, then came back into the kitchen. We traded items. My screen was completely shattered. I turned on the phone, and everything had been deleted and restored to factory settings.

Ken and Kathy gathered us together to pray. We participated. Once we were done, I walked out the door with the last bag of shoes in my hand.

5

WHEN WE DATED

September 2010

After a month talking back and forth on the phone, I decided to visit John in Houston. I told him the great news about my upcoming visit one night on the phone.

He was shocked. "You'd do that? That's really admirable of you to initiate coming here for a visit!"

I didn't think it was such a big deal. I traveled for work all the time. So I just replied, "Well, yeah—no problem!"

This was just one instance when John seemed shocked by my ease and kindness. It made me wonder what his other relationships had been like. During a phone conversation a few days later, I learned more about his past. It was my turn to be surprised.

"So, I have something to share with you that I think you should know," John began.

"Okay. Sure. What is it?"

"I have a daughter. I had her when I was very young," he quietly said.

"Oh, wow!" I blurted. "I mean, that's okay," I quickly added to reduce the shock in my voice. "How old she is?" I continued.

"She's nine."

"All right," I said. Again, I tried to make up for my reaction. "I'm sorry to sound so surprised. I just wasn't expecting you to say that."

"And there's something else," John interjected.

"What? Were you married too?" I jokingly asked.

"Yes, I was," John confirmed.

"What? Are you serious?" All I could do was laugh the shock away.

"Yeah, it was a silly thing I got myself into. It was more of an arrangement, and it shouldn't have happened. I was married for less than a year and divorced soon after," he explained.

I allowed the information to sit with me for a while. I listened as John explained the situation a bit more. It was actually quite an unfortunate situation. He and the mother of his child didn't get along, which impacted how often he could see his daughter.

We didn't talk a lot about it, though. I could tell John was uncomfortable talking about it, seeing as he didn't chalk it up to be a "real" marriage.

After we hung up, I was glad John had shared this personal information with me. It made me realize he thought of me as more than just a friend. Our relationship had gotten serious enough for him to let me into his life.

I had planned to take an early-morning flight to Houston so I could work remotely at John's house the rest of the day. My company had a location close to Houston, and I would work there the next day while John was at work. But I ended up missing my flight, which was the only direct route to Houston that day. I spent the morning at the airport, then took a flight later in the afternoon to Austin. I rented a car to drive to Houston and finally arrived at John's at nine o'clock that evening.

I knocked on John's door, relieved I actually made it. John gave me a hug, took my bags, and graciously invited me into his home. I sat on the couch in the living room and admired the décor in his home. I was surprised to see how well decorated John's home was—for a single guy.

"This is a very nice home," I eventually said.

"Thanks. I had some help with it," John humbly replied.

"Oh, nice. I was wondering," I truthfully replied with a little smile. He got the humor in it and smiled as well.

John had prepared dinner and kept it warming until I arrived. He had made salmon, rice, and salad. I was impressed.

We sat at the table for a lovely dinner, and afterward John showed me to my room upstairs. He shared that he hardly went upstairs in his house. His bedroom was downstairs, and he had no reason to leave the first floor. I thought that was cute.

John made me feel very comfortable in his presence. He was not like most guys, who would try to make a move. Rather, he was quite patient and respectful. Besides, I was not interested in taking things to the next level until marriage, and John shared the same view. If we were going to be in a relationship, we both wanted to commit to abstinence.

The next day, we returned the rental car, as John graciously invited me to use his car to drive downtown to the office. John had a truck he used to drive to work.

Throughout the day, I called John to check in. "Hey, how's your day going?" I asked when I called at three o'clock.

"Good. How's your day going?" John replied.

"Good as well. I'll leave here soon and go to the mall to pick up something, then I'll head back to the house. What time will you be home?"

"Oh, probably around five."

"Cool. I'll try to get back around the same time as well. Do you want anything while I'm out?"

"Um, no. I'm good." John sounded surprised. "You enjoy yourself."

"Okay, I will!"

"You are a woman to marry," John said quietly, though hoping I'd hear.

"Really? That's nice. Why do you say that?" I innocently asked.

"No reason. You'll find out later," John replied.

I just smiled. "I'll see you soon," I finally said as we hung up. John seemed to have liked something I said, but I wasn't sure what.

When I arrived back at his house and pulled up along the curb, John was just getting out of his truck in the driveway. He walked over to the car and greeted me with a bouquet of flowers and a kiss on the cheek.

On my last night in Houston, we went out to a seafood restaurant, then John surprised me with a drive to the ocean. John drove to a quiet spot by the rocks surrounding the ocean. He took out a small picnic basket from the back seat of the car, then took my hand to walk toward the ocean and find somewhere to sit to watch the waves.

"Wow, this is nice! Thank you," I said.

"You are very welcome," John replied.

He turned to get a bottle of wine and glasses from the picnic basket. Then he poured us each a glass.

"I'm really glad you're here. I've enjoyed our time together," John said as he turned back to me.

"Me too. It's been really nice," I sincerely replied.

I was truly happy I had decided to visit John. I felt completely comfortable in his presence.

John leaned in to me, held my face, and softly kissed my lips. It was the most romantic, gentle, enduring first kiss I'd ever experienced.

"You are a good man, Mr. John," I said with a giggle and smile while still looking into his eyes.

The next day, John took me to the airport, confident we'd see each other again soon. I returned to Houston the following month for a weekend visit. This time, I researched places John and I could go so I could plan a surprise date for Saturday evening.

I was slightly disappointed, though, when John left me at the house all day Saturday while he worked. He knew I would be there that weekend, yet he hadn't taken the time off.

John was very apologetic, explaining the nature of his construction job. I understood that construction often included weekends. But still, I knew he could have taken the day off if he had wanted. I bet he would have taken it off if he had been feeling a little under the weather or if he had an important appointment. So why wouldn't he do that for me?

I eventually put that behind me so we could enjoy the evening I had planned. Even John had to ask where I found the place. It was a beautiful historic Spanish restaurant with live music.

"Did I do good?" I asked him.

"Yes, you did. This is very nice!" John replied.

"So," I began, "we've been talking to each other for a few months, and we've spent time together during my visits here. I was wondering, how do you feel about things?"

I was eager to hear John express how he felt about me and our relationship. We hadn't officially defined it yet.

"I feel good about things," John simply replied.

I knew John was a man of few words, but even for him, this was too little. A month earlier, he'd referenced marriage. Now he seemed apprehensive about expressing himself. He was purposely saying as few words as possible.

I thought this was a typical man thing. I decided to take another approach to our conversation.

"Okay. Well, would you say we are in a relationship?"

"Would you?"

"I'm asking *you*. I would like you to answer the question," I replied, wondering why this was becoming so difficult.

After a momentarily pause, John finally said, "Yes, I would say we are in a relationship."

"Good! That's nice to know!" I smiled to tease John.

However, I couldn't help but think, *If I hadn't asked, would John have said anything?*

The following month, John traveled to Belleville to visit me instead. He had a chance to meet my parents, which went really well. John made a good impression, and my parents were pleased to get to know him. John seemed to like them as well. I was relieved that he seemed more comfortable in our relationship now. We shared some fun moments hanging out downtown and going skating.

Soon it was December. It had been three months since we established our relationship. John decided to travel back to Belleville to spend the holidays with me and my family. We took holiday pictures together and even baked a cake that we shared with my parents on New Year's Eve.

"When would you want to get married?" John suddenly asked as we were sitting on the couch in my parents' basement.

"Next December would be nice! Maybe the twelfth day of the twelfth month. That would be cool! What about you?"

"I like that too. That would be a good time," John agreed.

"Okay, let's keep that in our minds. We have a date!" I replied, smiling back at John, realizing we both wanted to marry each other.

6

THE DAY AFTER I LEFT

February 2015

After seeing John's behavior, it was clear to everyone that he no longer wanted me in the home or as part of the restaurant. His cold and distant attitude said a lot more than he did. His selfishness and pride were apparent in his unwillingness to even listen to Kathy and Ken. John believed he was better than I was. He felt he was completely right in the situation; therefore, he felt his actions were justified. He had convinced himself that he was doing what was best. He never considered that maybe this situation was happening so he could become more aware of himself.

After I packed all my things from the house, Kathy and Ken came with me to Cherie's place, where I would stay that night. Kathy and Ken expressed how John's behavior surprised and disappointed them. For all the years they had known John, they had never known that side of him.

Throughout our marriage, I often felt John kept me in a box separate from the other aspects of his life. There was the John I saw, and then there was the John his family, friends, and even daughter would see. It never felt transparent. Seeing Kathy and Ken's reaction now, it was becoming evident no one had a true knowledge of John.

Cherie was nice enough to give me a towel and a toothbrush so I didn't have to dig through the boxes and bags I had moved to her garage. Once I settled in on Cherie's couch for the night, I realized I hadn't thoroughly looked in my wallet after John grabbed it and tossed it on the garage floor.

I reached for it now—my permanent resident card was gone. I next went to the garage and looked in my jewelry box—my engagement ring and wedding band were gone. Then I looked in the folder where I kept all my personal documents—my passport and social security card were gone.

John had taken everything. He must have gone through my things one night while he had me locked out of the bedroom. Although I was banished to the couch, I had still kept my things in the bedroom. I never thought John would go through my things, much less take them. Especially my government documents.

My heart thumped in disbelief. What was John thinking? It seemed he wanted to strip me of anything remotely associated with him, not to mention make sure I wasn't able to do anything without him.

I checked a side slit in my folder, looking for the blank check I had taken from the restaurant checkbook. It too was missing. John had apparently dug through my folder thoroughly enough to even find the check.

I had stashed the blank check to make sure the loan payments continued. About two years earlier, I had loaned John $80,000 to help start the restaurant. We used restaurant funds to make the payments, but the loan was still in my name. It was one of the many sacrifices I had made for him.

When I took the check, I wasn't sure what I would do with it—whether I would use it pay off the loan or to hold it as leverage over John. In either case, I didn't want the restaurant to go out of business. I just wanted something to ensure John would do the right thing if the time came for us to separate. But now the check was gone. This was not good.

I sent John an email.

Subject: Missing items from wallet

John,
I was going through my wallet and noticed that my permanent residence card is missing. Do you have it?

In the morning, I tried calling John. He didn't answer. I phoned Ken to let him know I was missing my important documents. I asked if he could call John to see if he could get them back.

After that call, my phone suddenly got cut off. John managed our cell phones under the family plan. Once he realized I could still use my phone, he called the phone company to disconnect it.

I dug into my boxes in Cherie's garage to get my internet phone. I had to connect it because I had an interview at noon. But something was wrong; Cherie's internet connection wouldn't work with my phone. I could receive calls but couldn't hear the person on the other end. I spent most of the morning trying to fix it before my interview.

The interview was something I had kept to myself. I had been searching for a job for the past eight months, with no luck. I didn't tell John about this interview because I was starting to think he had been somehow sending bad vibes in my direction.

I was excited about the interview. It was my fifth round of interviewing for the position, so I was pretty confident. This job was exactly what I wanted. It was in Houston, which is where I thought I should stay rather than going back home to Belleville. It had little to no travel, which I loved. I had spent seven years traveling in my previous job.

After the interview, Ken called.

"Well, I spoke to John this morning," he said. "He's upset with me. He asked how I could take sides. I let him know Kathy and I were there to help the situation, not to take any sides. There are no sides to take here. We're just trying to help a bad situation find resolution. Anyway, I tried to talk to him, but he wasn't saying much. I asked him about your documents and told him he needs to return them. He said he didn't have them. Actually, he said he has a restraining order against you. If you come to the house, you will be arrested."

My mouth dropped.

"Wow. Really? What is wrong with him?" I asked in shock.

"I don't know. I don't know what's going on in John's head right now. But it's not good. I suggest you try getting the documents some other way," Ken said with disappointment.

After we hung up, I just sat there. What could I do? I had nothing.

I called Cherie at work to let her know what Ken had told me. She suggested I call the police. So I did.

I told them about the incident in the garage between John and me, that I had left the house, and that my documents were missing. I let them know that all I wanted were my documents; I didn't care about anything else.

Just as the officer started speaking, my internet phone cut off.

"Oh, damn!" I exclaimed.

Cherie had encouraged me to use her extra car, so I decided to go directly to the police station. When I got there, they wouldn't let me speak to someone in person. Instead, they gave me a card with a number to call. It was the same number I had already dialed.

So I returned to Cherie's house to call the police once again. At least I was able to speak to the same officer as before. She said that once the phone cut off, she had sent a police car over to check on me. But of course, they missed me because I was on my way to the station. The whole situation was ridiculous. But I didn't have time to think about how crazy things had gotten. I was in action mode, just doing what I needed to do.

Because of the restraining order John supposedly had issued, I couldn't go to the house by myself, but the officer said I could go with a police escort. I said I'd call once I knew he had arrived home after work.

That evening became a stakeout. I parked the car down the street, waiting until I saw John come home. An hour passed before I saw lights appear inside the kitchen. I quickly called the police, but another forty-five minutes passed before they arrived. The entire time, I was anxious and nervous, hoping John hadn't gone to bed early.

When the officer finally arrived, I drove Cherie's car back to her house just down the street, then walked to John's house with the officer. I asked the police officer to go to the door first while I stood back. I didn't think John would answer the door if he saw me.

Knock. Knock.

When the door opened, I came around the corner and walked up to the front door with the officer.

"I'm here with Justyne to gather her belongings. Do you have her passport and other documents?" the officer asked sternly.

"What? Passport? I don't have those things," John deniably responded.

"We are going to come inside and give Justyne an opportunity to gather anything she needs. She is entitled to a one-time visit to get her belongings," the officer informed John.

First, I went into the bedroom to look through the drawers. I noticed a safe on the floor I had never seen before. I let the officer know, and he made John open it to see if my documents were in there, which they weren't.

Next, I went upstairs to get my wedding dress from under the bed in the guest room. I had plans to sell it as soon as possible.

I came back downstairs and went in the garage. Blossom was in the kitchen. I walked past her as if she were air in my way. Next to the garbage was a package for me that had come in the mail. I went through the rest of the garbage and found other personal items John hadn't wasted time in throwing away.

I turned to the police officer once he came into the garage.

"Isn't it illegal for someone to throw away mail that doesn't belong to them?" I asked, already knowing the answer.

"No, not unless it's placed outside for trash pickup," the officer replied.

I was not impressed with his response. It was quite obvious that the package had been placed for trash. Plus, we didn't even have trash pickup in the neighborhood. We had to bring our own trash to the garbage site.

I went back inside, passed Blossom again, and went to the front door.

"Is there anything else?" the officer asked.

"No, but I still don't have my documents," I reminded him, fighting back my anxiety and frustration.

The officer paused. "Please wait outside so I can talk to your husband."

When the officer was done, he walked out to the driveway, where I stood waiting.

"I asked John about your documents again, but he said he didn't have them," he informed me with a lax tone. "There's nothing else I can do."

I walked back to Cherie's house to ponder my next move. I held my head down for a moment, feeling defeated. All the officer had done was simply ask John about the documents. I don't know why he hadn't been more forceful in searching the house. Now I could only hope I would somehow find my documents so I didn't have to worry anymore. I felt disgusted and emotionally drained. I just wanted to go to sleep.

The next morning, Cherie received a text from John. He said he had dropped off some stuff I had left at the house. It was by her doorstep.

I opened the door to find my body pillow, a painting, and my passport.

7

WHEN WE GOT ENGAGED

February to September 2011

It had been six months since the Montreal festival, where John and I reconnected. Now we were enrolled in premarital classes at John's church in Houston. It was evident that we both had good intentions for this relationship to lead to marriage. Although John hadn't proposed yet, we decided to attend the classes to learn more about each other and prepare for marriage.

Taking real steps toward marriage with John was refreshing but surreal. It made me think about how close Michael and I had come to getting married yet how much I struggled to get him to settle down and commit to our relationship.

Four months before John and I first met in Las Vegas, I was in Atlanta celebrating my birthday with Michael. I remember being so anxious, expecting Michael to propose that day. I woke up to breakfast in bed—Michael surprised me with a beautiful breakfast arrangement and flowers.

Later that day, we drove about thirty minutes up north to a lake. When Michael parked the car, I looked around at the beautiful scenery of trees, horses, and the crystal-blue lake.

"Okay, my lady. Are you ready for your birthday horseback ride?" Michael asked in his always charming, humorous way. His personality was always uplifting and adoring. He kept me smiling.

"Yes, I am!" I eagerly replied with a big smile on my face.

We walked hand in hand up a small hill to the horse barn to saddle up. The private horseback ride was about sixty minutes into the forest, and it ended in a secluded area by the lake, where a picnic had been set up. Michael had this all planned out. I was quite impressed. But I was still very anxious, thinking, *When is he going to pop the question?*

We ate the picnic, then took a canoe ride on the lake. *Okay, this is it*, I thought. I didn't speak. I didn't move. I tried not to do anything that would delay Michael's asking me the big question.

"Are you enjoying the ride?" he asked, trying to make small talk in the awkward silence.

"Yes." I kept my words short.

We canoed for a while. I could tell Michael was hesitating. He kept making silly jokes. Now I was getting quite annoyed.

"Aren't you going to ask me?"

I couldn't wait any longer—I just asked Michael point-blank.

"Ask you what?" he replied as if not knowing what I was talking about.

"Are you serious? I thought you were going to ask me to marry you!" I honestly replied.

"Why would you ever think that?" Michael said with a straight face. "Why can't you just enjoy the day?" he added, then got quiet.

Now I was pissed. He just said the wrong thing to me. Not only did he kill my anticipation about a proposal but he also just threw it to the side. I was ready to go ashore, get out of this canoe, and go home. And that's exactly what I did.

It wasn't the same ride we'd had on the way there. There was complete silence. I could feel the disappointment in Michael's heart.

Suddenly, he spoke. "You know, I had planned a dinner afterward for us, but you just ruined it." He wasn't smiling.

I felt bad. Really bad.

We got back to Michael's home, and he went straight into the living room. I went upstairs to put my things away. A few minutes later, I went back downstairs.

"Perhaps we can still go to dinner," I offered, trying to smooth things over.

"No," Michael said flat out.

Again, I was mad at myself and at him. Like a child, I stormed upstairs, cursing and shouting out loud. "I'm trying to make things better, but you just want to stay mad! Look how long we've been together—yet you still don't want to propose. I'm wasting my time with you! I can't do this anymore—I can't keep playing house with you. This is foolishness! I'm worth more than this. I'm going home, then!"

Everything I thought and felt came out, whether it was right or wrong.

In tears, I started packing. I was overwhelmed by my own anxiousness and fears. Michael came into the room to calm me down and stop me from packing. Suddenly, he got down on one knee and pulled out a box with a ring.

"I want you to marry me. Will you marry me, Justyne?" he asked. Fear of losing me was in his eyes.

I was shocked. He had a ring. He proposed.

"Oh my goodness, Michael. Are you doing this because you want to or because you feel you have to?"

Without answering, Michael put the ring on my finger, and we hugged. But the next few minutes were awkward. I knew Michael wasn't pleased that the proposal and the whole day hadn't gone as planned. I think he had actually planned to propose at some point during the day, perhaps at the lake or later at dinner.

I too felt weird. I was happy but felt guilty at the same time. I knew my actions didn't deserve the proposal and ring.

Michael suggested I still fly home to give us time to cool off and think. I was nervous to leave his side, but I ended up going home the following day.

Feelings were strained between us for the next couple of months. Michael wanted another chance to propose when the time and moment was right for him, so he took back the ring.

Knowing Michael had the ring and intentions to propose, I constantly thought about our future together and wondered when it would start. December of that year was especially rough. It marked another year gone by without us moving forward.

A part of me was scared we'd end up like Michael's brother and his girlfriend. They had been together for several years, got engaged, then ended up breaking up. I feared the same thing would happen to us. I truly allowed my fears and negativity to strain the relationship.

On Christmas Eve, Michael's family hosted dinner at their home in Belleville. Michael came home for the holidays to spend time with me and his family. I always enjoyed spending the holidays with his family. They were a big, close family and very welcoming.

I remember sitting on the couch and suddenly starting to cry. I just wanted to be together so badly.

Michael came over and sat beside me, leaning in to see my face. "Why are you crying?"

"I want you to ask me to marry you. I want us to be married," I replied, trying to hide my tears.

Michael put his arm around me to console my sadness, then he suggested we go for a drive so we could talk. He stopped at a park, then took out the ring.

"I've been carrying this ring around because I know I want to be with you. I don't think this proposal will ever go the way I want it to go, so it doesn't make sense to prolong it anymore. I want us to be married—and we will be," Michael said assuredly. "Will you marry me?"

"I want to be with you too! Yes, I'll marry you!"

It was official.

We spent the rest of the night in each other's arms, and we told his parents the following morning before I went home.

When I got home later that day, I sat at the kitchen table and showed my parents my engagement ring.

"What's that?" my mother said in a very unhappy tone. "If it's a ring you want, I'll go and get one for you." She shook her head and carried on. "You are not going to marry Michael. Is this how you people do things? You never told me you were in a relationship with Michael. And he didn't come to ask us for permission."

My mother's issues with Michael went back to when we were teenagers. Not because of anything he did. It was something beyond our understanding. It appeared Michael did not meet my mother's great expectations for what she envisioned and wanted for me. Although nothing is perfect, it had to be for her daughter. Nothing but the best.

My mother was never happy about the idea of Michael and me being more than just friends, so I didn't share much of our relationship with her. It made me feel disconnected from my mother and somewhat resentful of the control she insisted to have over my life. When Michael tried to talk to my parents one night years earlier, my mother stayed upstairs, refusing to speak with him. At least my dad was more reasonable. He listened to Michael express how he felt about me and his intentions. Still, there was a battle on my side, and Michael and I had to be strong in order to endure.

In contrast, Michael's family embraced me and our relationship. This created a respect issue between our parents. Even though our parents were friends, Michael's mother never spoke to my mother about our relationship. She didn't want to make the situation more uncomfortable.

Although my parents didn't approve, it didn't stop me from wanting to marry the man I loved. Not long after New Year's, I went to Atlanta to visit Michael, my new fiancé. I thought it would be a good time to discuss a budget and potential dates and locations for our upcoming wedding.

Michael declared the budget would be $5,000, the wedding would be in two years, and he'd need to speak to his mom about location.

I paused. I took a breath. But my anxiety and frustration rose nonetheless. I thought this was Michael's way of stalling because he really didn't want to get married.

I started to freak out. Things got out of hand—the words that came out of my mouth didn't come out well.

With that, Michael was done talking about the wedding. He went upstairs. I was left in the living room feeling confused and angry. I kept thinking the wedding wouldn't happen. Michael needed time, but I didn't know how to give it to him.

The next day was even more horrible. I ended up throwing the ring back at Michael and calling off the wedding. I didn't think I would see that ring again.

Just a couple of months later, we reconnected in Las Vegas. It meant a lot to me. I thought it was the beginning of us getting back on track. But it became clear that Michael didn't feel the same.

After seeing each other in Las Vegas, it was close to a year and a half before I saw Michael again. Michael emailed me, stating how he had been thinking about me. Although he was dating someone, he couldn't stop thinking about us being together. I was dating someone as well at the time and told Michael this.

A few weeks passed, and I was working on a project in Saint Louis. Michael emailed again. He was in town and wanted to see me. I was surprised and flattered at the same time.

That evening, we met for dinner. Most of the conversation was spent talking about what had happened in the past and how much he had hurt me. Michael became obviously uncomfortable.

We took a taxi to the hotel, and Michael walked me back to my room. I asked if he wanted to come inside awhile to hang out. He did. We continued talking, then out of the blue, Michael got down on his knee to propose. Again.

"You are the only person I have ever loved and will ever love. I want us to be together," Michael professed with tears almost in his eyes.

"Are you serious? Do you really meant it?" I asked as my heart pounded.

"Yes, I mean it. I love you," Michael replied.

"Yes, I will marry you!" I smiled and gave Michael a hug.

We kissed and embraced in awe. I looked at the ring I thought I would never see again. I noticed Michael had it engraved with the code 143, which meant "I love you."

We spent the night in each other's arms, similar to that Christmas night a year and a half earlier. Michael had a flight out the next morning. He had literally just bought a ticket for a day to see me.

I traveled back home and called my girlfriends to tell them the news. I was happy again. I had limited conversations with the guy I was dating. I tried to avoid saying anything until I knew exactly what to say.

That Saturday, I stayed home, anticipating I'd spend the evening talking to Michael. I called twice but didn't get an answer. I waited an hour before I called back and finally got him.

"Sorry. I was at the gym when you called earlier," he said before I even asked about the missed calls. He had a response ready.

"Oh, okay. No problem. How was your day?" I asked.

We continued the small talk for some time, until I realized Michael sounded different. His responses were short, and there were more pauses in between sentences than usual. It seemed he wanted to say something.

"What's up, Michael? Are you okay?" I finally asked.

"Uh, yeah. There is something I want to tell you, actually," Michael hesitantly said.

"All right," I replied.

"Yeah . . ." he began. "I kinda made a mistake. I kinda shouldn't have proposed. I did that hastily, and I shouldn't have. It was a mistake on my part, and for that, I'm sorry."

I was frozen. I took a breath.

"You *made a mistake*? You bought a plane ticket, booked yourself a hotel room, got the ring engraved, brought the ring with you, proposed . . . and it was a *mistake*?"

I didn't even hear Michael trying to interrupt me to explain himself. I just continued.

"You sick, twisted asshole! You poor excuse for a man! You effing made a mistake? An effing mistake! Who does that? What kind of man are you? Do you even know what you want? You listen to me—don't you ever call me, ever again. You are dead to me. You hear me? Dead."

Click. I hung up. I blocked Michael's number and directed his email address to the trash folder to be sure I never heard from him again. I sold the ring on eBay.

In the months to come, I devoted my energy to forgetting about Michael. I was good at it for about five months, until I got the urge to call him. I wasn't sure why. I think it was for closure.

Michael was surprised to hear from me. He said he had tried to contact me but had never heard back. Which was true. He had sent emails and texts to apologize, but I'd ignored them all.

I let Michael know I was going to Miami in a few weeks for a little relaxing time. We barely spoke after that call, but a day before my trip, Michael let me know he had booked a ticket to meet me in Miami.

The resort where I had reserved my suite conveniently accommodated Michael as well. We had separate rooms. However, I quickly realized this was a trip for closure.

Being with Michael wasn't the same anymore. The one person I thought would never hurt me, did. My heart wasn't the same. I couldn't trust Michael with my life or my heart anymore.

The three days was like putting together a 1,600-piece puzzle. We could get only the corners together to hold a conversation. There wasn't enough time to put the middle pieces in place.

Michael left for his flight early in the morning. He knocked on my door to say good-bye. We hugged, and I knew in that moment our journey together was over.

I arrived back home from Miami with a closure I hadn't felt before. After fifteen years in an on-and-off relationship with Michael, my mind and heart were ready for the next chapter in my life. I was at peace and satisfied.

A few months later, I received the Facebook message from John letting me know he would be in Montreal that summer.

And now here we were, preparing for marriage. One thing we had in common was wanting to be married. We both diligently pursued the end goal. We started reading Gary Chapman's *Things I Wish I'd*

Known Before We Got Married, and we enrolled in the twelve-week premarital class with the pastor at John's church.

In the first few classes, we had conversations with the pastor so we could get to know each other a bit more. My work schedule was flexible, so I could travel back and forth to Houston to be there in person for the sessions.

One time I was there, John was planning a concert at his church. He asked if I would help him work the front door to manage the tickets. Of course, I was happy to help.

As I took my position at the entrance, I was greeted by a young woman also working the door. She seemed shocked to see me. I could tell she was instantly uncomfortable and anxious. When John came around, she couldn't get to him fast enough to give him a hug. I stood back and watched. At one point, she pulled out her cell phone, and I noticed her wallpaper was a picture of her and John.

It took me a moment, but I remembered John telling me about a girl he used to date. He said the relationship was over but that the girl was still attached to him. I put two and two together. This had to be her.

The fact that she was apparently stalking John was one thing—but the fact that he had enlisted her help with the concert was another. I couldn't help but be upset by the situation. At the very least, John shouldn't have put me in that situation without alerting me. The whole night, she kept asking me questions and wasn't shy about letting me know her feelings about John.

I decided not to say anything to John at the concert. Rather, I would wait until we had a private moment together.

John's sister Veronica had arrived from out of town that day to help with the concert. It was the first time I'd met her. After the concert, she drove me back to the house while John dropped off the performers at the airport.

Veronica noticed my irritation. "What's wrong?"

"Oh, nothing. It's okay," I replied, not wanting to get into it.

"No. I can tell you're upset about something. What's wrong?" Veronica insisted.

"I'll be okay." My responses were getting shorter.

"Was it something that happened tonight?" Veronica further insisted.

"Why? Did something happen tonight that I *should* be upset about?" I asked, wanting to see what she'd say.

"I don't know. Is there?" Veronica responded right back.

"Look, I don't want to disrespect anyone, so I'll deal with it later," I finally said to stop the back-and-forth interrogation. I wasn't going to express my feelings to someone I'd just met that day. And I wasn't sure if Veronica's insistence was coming from a place of genuine concern or rude intrusiveness.

When we pulled up to the driveway, John was right behind. When we all walked into the house, the kitchen was a mess.

"Oh, I know John doesn't like dishes in the sink," Veronica said loudly.

It seemed she was trying to tell me how to keep John happy. I rolled my eyes and didn't reply. All I could think was that his sister should be minding her own business.

I went into the living room and sat on the couch. John could see I was visibly upset, yet he still walked past me and went to bed. I tried calling him from the guest bedroom, but he didn't answer.

The next morning, we all got ready for church. I told John I wanted to speak to him before we left, so we met in the kitchen. With his sister still around, it was the closest we would have to privacy.

"The girl last night helping at the front entrance—is she the girl you used to date?" I asked, getting straight to the point.

"Yes," John replied without hesitation.

"Why didn't you tell me she'd be there? I was very uncomfortable in that situation," I expressed honestly.

John apologized, but I got the feeling he thought I was overreacting. I continued to express my feelings about the situation to be sure John understood how I felt, and he listened, continuing to say "I'm sorry" where he could. In any case, we were able to talk about it, so I put it behind me.

We went to our premarital class that afternoon. This session was the most revealing so far. John and I had completed an assessment to determine our personality styles. The pastor used the results to help us understand how we reacted in different situations and how our personalities complemented each other. As we sat there in his office, the pastor seemed to dig deep into my soul.

"If someone does something to hurt you, do you find it hard to forgive them?" the pastor asked, looking directly at me.

"Well, yes, I guess. It's hard to forgive someone who hurts me because I feel I would never do that to them," I replied innocently, not knowing the true meaning of what I just said.

"Ah, hm . . ." he replied, stroking his chin.

I was nervous because I didn't understand what he had discovered from my response.

The pastor looked next at John.

"You see, a flower that is not nourished withers and eventually dies. Because of Justyne's temperament, you need to treat her like a delicate flower. You need to water a flower in order for it to grow. You see, Justyne will always tell you the temperature, but you need to be the thermostat to adjust the temperature. She won't be able to do it herself."

Oh my goodness. The pastor's words penetrated through me. In that moment, I felt understood. Completely understood. I felt John grab for my hand to comfort me. I think he got it too.

John and I continued to work on our relationship by spending more time together whenever we could. We also made an effort to be with various friends and family. Given the distance in our relationship, we communicated a lot via email. When we wanted to discuss something important and we needed the other person's undivided attention, we titled the email "express yourself."

As our relationship progressed, I began to feel communication in general was becoming a factor. I decided to send him an "express yourself" email.

Subject: Express Yourself

Hey, John,

Hope your day is going well! Something has been on my mind, and I wanted to share it with you.

I believe communication is important and that it is the lifeline in a relationship. I have concerns in how we communicate. I'm not comfortable with the way things are going. I don't expect you to "get it" overnight or for things to be perfect, but I would hope we can start with an understanding and an acknowledgment that we "hear" each other.

Anyway, I don't want to get into much through email, but I just wanted to give you insight into what I'm feeling. I came across this website (5lovelanguges. com), and it confirmed to me how real and important it is to understand how to communicate to each other . . . Hope you find time to read it.

Enjoy the rest of your day,

Justyne

John called me. "I get it. I'll try to do better," he attested.

A few months later, John came to Belleville for my graduation from my master's program. I decided to throw a BBQ party to celebrate and to give my friends an opportunity to meet John.

As I was preparing the food for the party, John made remarks along the way, such as "You use oil instead of butter in the water before putting in the corn," and "I've never seen chicken put on the BBQ like that before! I usually do it like *this*."

I eventually turned to John and said as nicely as I could, "Don't worry about it. It's okay. You should go relax before people get here."

John quickly said okay and walked away.

When people started to arrive, John was not around. I went downstairs to the basement and found him sitting soberly on the couch.

"Hey, why are you here? People are starting to arrive."

"Yeah, okay," he replied.

"What's wrong?"

"Well, it's like you don't want my help. I don't like feeling useless. I was trying to help you, and it's like you didn't want it," John expressed.

I was surprised by John's reaction to the situation. He was truly upset, but I didn't understand why.

"It's not like I didn't want your help. I just felt like you wanted to do things your way rather than help me. And besides, you're my guest too, so I didn't want you to feel you had to do a lot of work," I honestly explained, hoping it would mend the situation.

John took a minute before he got up from the couch and eventually came upstairs to greet my friends. The rest of the evening went well, ending with John and me cleaning up and watching a movie.

After John headed back home, my parents let me know he had pulled them aside and asked them for my hand in marriage. I was excited that it was actually happening, not to mention flattered that he was gentleman enough to ask my parents.

The next few months were nerve-racking, though. Each time we were together, I anticipated the moment John would pop the question. It was a feeling I was too familiar with, given my history with Michael. It was happening all over again.

A close family friend was getting married in Jamaica. My whole family went to celebrate. As I rounded every corner, I expected John to pop up and surprise me. I thought it would be so nice if John came to Jamaica to propose with my family present. But he never showed up.

When I got home, I called John to share my concerns and doubts. It was August, and he hadn't proposed, yet we were already looking for a venue for a wedding in December. I was feeling more and more anxious.

I guess my expression of doubt was too much for him. John got upset and felt pushed to the point of saying something.

"If you're so concerned about when I'm going to propose, then you should know I was planning on doing it on our trip to Washington, DC, next weekend!" he blurted out. Then he hung up.

When I met up with John at the Washington, DC, airport, he didn't look too happy to see me. I greeted him with the biggest smile and hug anyway. We joined up with his friends and spent the next two days sightseeing. We went for a bike ride around the White House and downtown monuments. We went to the Martin Luther King monument twice.

The second time we were at the monument, John said he had forgotten something there the first time. I parked my bike and looked behind me. John was holding a ring in his hand.

"Well, you already knew this was coming," John said with a smile.

"Oh my goodness!" I exclaimed, then waited for him to continue.

John was still smiling, but he seemed out of sorts. He didn't know what else to say. Because he had revealed his plan to propose, he now felt he had lost the moment.

I may have known he would propose sometime on this trip, but I didn't know how. I was genuinely surprised. He still had a chance to make the moment his own.

"Could you get on one knee?" I asked, nudging him to what I thought he may have wanted to do.

"Will you marry me, Justyne?" John asked on bended knee.

"Yes, of course!" I gave John a big hug and kiss. I was truly happy.

8

THE WEEK AFTER I LEFT

February 2015

Now that I had my passport, I was able to start the process of getting my social security and permanent residence cards replaced. For whatever reason, John hadn't returned those to me along with my passport.

Later that day, I received a job offer from the company I had been interviewing with. I would start on Monday. I was elated that things were coming together. My mind was so focused on what I needed to get done that I didn't have time to think about John and his horrific antics. I also started searching for a place I could rent in Houston so I wouldn't have to keep crashing at Cherie's. I knew she didn't mind, but I still wanted to be mindful.

I was happy too that my college friend Trish was in town from Barbados for the weekend. We had a chance to get our nails done, go shopping, go out to dinner—do all the things I'd missed while being consumed with the restaurant every day. I took Trish to the airport Monday morning, on my way to my first day at work.

I spent that first day in an online orientation session. After lunch, I received an email requesting my IDs to verify my employment. I had my driver's license and passport, but nothing else. I let them know my other documents had been taken from me and that I was in the process of getting them replaced. They said I could have two more days to get everything together.

I submitted an application to replace my permanent resident card. The immigration office assured me the application would be a valid form of identification until the new card was processed. I sent a copy of the application to my company.

The next day after returning home from work, I received a phone call from Beth in human resources to inform me that I had been terminated. According to them, the application was not valid identification.

As I sat there holding the phone, my heart sank. I'd rushed to pay $450 for the application for the sole purpose of providing it to the company as identification, and now they said it wasn't valid.

"I was told that providing proof that my card had been stolen or damaged was sufficient evidence," I said to the human resources representative with my heart pounding loudly.

"No, I'm afraid it isn't," Beth said apologetically. "We spent over two hours with the employment verification department. They told us it wasn't valid. So without any way to show your employment status, we have to process your termination."

"I still have one more day to verify my employment, correct?" I asked.

"Yes. But I don't know what else you could do at this point. They already told us that we can't accept what you sent," she insisted.

"Please give me until tomorrow to see what else I can do. I wouldn't feel right if I didn't try everything possible to resolve this. Please, I'm begging you," I pleaded as though my life depended on it.

If only they knew, it kinda did.

"Okay. We'll give you until tomorrow. But your computer access will be turned off until then," Beth concluded.

"Thank you."

I hung up in total shock. I couldn't believe this was happening. I couldn't be losing this job. I had told my mom and friends about this new job. That weekend, I had put down a security deposit on an apartment I'd found to rent; I was scheduled to move in a few days.

It took me a moment to think of my next step. In desperation, I phoned John, thinking I could plead with him to give me back my documents. He didn't answer. I then sent Cherie a text, asking her to contact John to try getting my documents.

I sat in the chair for a minute to think of what else I could do. I decided to call the employment verification department to inquire for myself. I was connected to Brent from customer service. I explained my situation and what the human resources representative told me.

"I'm not sure who your HR rep spoke to," Brent stated, "but it is clearly written that an application showing that you're getting your resident card replaced is valid. And you have up to ninety days to reverify, to allow time for you to receive your new card."

"Could I connect you with my HR rep so you can explain this to her directly?" I asked.

"Yes, of course," Brent cheerfully replied.

Keeping Brent on the line, I dialed Beth to join the call. We discussed the situation for about half an hour, until Beth was satisfied with the information.

"I'm so sorry about this mix-up, Justyne," she said. "I'll confirm the information Brent has provided and will follow up with you in the morning."

As soon as the call ended, I just started to cry. Tears poured down my face. It was the first time I had cried since leaving John. I was trying to just move on from this mess, and it was more challenging than I'd thought it would be. John was doing everything he could to control me, when all I wanted was to do the right thing to move on.

That night, I couldn't eat, and I barely slept. My mind stayed awake, anticipating what kind of call I would receive the following morning.

I heard Cherie's girls getting ready for school around seven o'clock. I decided to get up too. I went downstairs and started watching the morning shows. Cherie wished me well before she headed off to work. It was 11:07 a.m. when the phone finally rang.

"Hi, Justyne. It's Beth from HR. I was able to verify the information from Brent, and we have reset your employee profile. You are good to return to work and rejoin the training this week. We're sorry for the confusion."

"Thank you! I apologize as well for the mix-up," I said, feeling quite embarrassed.

We ended the conversation on a good note. Hanging up, I said a thankful prayer, grateful for getting my job back. For the rest of the day, I got caught up with the training I missed.

Later, at 11:55 p.m. that night, we were all upstairs in bed when a knock came on the front door. I jumped up, thinking it might be John, seeing as he lived a few doors down the street. I went out into the hall to see Cherie in her adult onesie, wondering who was knocking on the door at this late hour. We both went downstairs.

"Who is it?" Cherie yelled from inside.

"It's Chief Thompson from the police department," the male voice outside responded.

Cherie and I looked at each other in complete confusion. Cherie opened the door.

"Hello. Is Justyne Black here?" the officer asked, looking at me. It was the same officer who had gone with me to the house to get my belongings. He held some papers.

"Yes, that's me," I confirmed.

"Justyne Black, this is a summons to appear in court in regard to a restraining order filed against you by John Black—"

"*What?*" I interrupted the officer midsentence.

When John told Ken he got a restraining order, a part of me didn't believe it to be true. I thought it was just John trying to intimidate me.

"Yes, John Black filed a restraining order against you for domestic violence. I'll review the restraining order with you: You are to stay five hundred yards away from the house, the restaurant that is the place of business, and the church located on 2923 North Central Street." The officer continued, "The court date is scheduled on Friday, February 13, at 1:30 p.m." The officer looked at his watch. "So that is later today. Sorry for the late notice—we didn't have time to come out here sooner to give this to you," the officer concluded.

"Okay. Thank you." I took the papers from the officer, ended the conversation, and closed the door.

Immediately, Cherie turned to me and said, "Don't worry about this. I'll help you figure out what you need to do."

I had no words.

After only a couple of hours of sleep, I got out of bed early to start preparing for my court appearance later that day. I contacted my trainer at work to let him know I wouldn't be able to attend the orientation session that day because of the sudden court appearance. I asked if I could make other arrangements. We decided I would contact him when I got back from court, and he would catch me up. I said I was happy to work after hours to make up the time.

I started to put together information to outline the truth behind what had happened in the garage. John had a way of leaving out key information when telling a story. He made it seem I scratched him for no reason. I guess he forgot to mention how he had grabbed my bag, pulled me out of the car, flipped my bag upside down, shook it, and took my phone and things out of my wallet. Apparently, he didn't acknowledge that was why I accidentally scratched him as I tried to get my bag back.

I got to the courthouse and signed in to indicate my attendance. I didn't see John; he hadn't arrived yet. I sat in the main waiting area about ten minutes, then I heard my name.

"Justyne Black. Justyne Black," an officer yelled out.

When I approached the desk, the officer informed me that I had to go to a separate waiting area down the hall. Because John had filed a domestic violence restraining order against me, I had to be a certain distance from him, given he was the "victim" in the situation.

I walked to the other room, which was empty. A few minutes later, two men came in to find a seat. I of course didn't know their stories. Perhaps they were being unfairly accused. Or perhaps they were actual domestic violence offenders.

Then they started to talk to each other, seemingly about the incident that brought them here. One of the men shouted, "I don't care what she says. If she'd just left me alone, then that wouldn't have happened. I don't care. Just make sure she leaves me alone!"

Yet there I was, Justyne Wilson from Belleville, Canada, sitting in a waiting room with these men, awaiting to stand before a judge and defend myself in a domestic violence charge filed by my husband. I chuckled a bit. It was just that ridiculous.

An officer came in to get me. The court was ready for my case. I walked into the quiet courtroom. Other officers were in the room. John sat on the right side, and the judge sat in the center. I was instructed to sit at the table on the left side.

The judge opened the case with her remarks, then asked John if he still wanted to pursue the case. John responded yes. The judge allowed John to speak first.

It was like a scene from the movies. John began to tell his story. He had medical reports and blown-up pictures of the scratch on his face. It was like hearing a little boy tell about how a kid in the playground threw sand. He even told the judge that after he showed me the scratch, I told him to go get a Band-Aid. Which I did! What was wrong with that? It was pathetic that John thought that would carry weight on his case. Was I really sitting in court because of a scratch on his forehead that didn't require stitches?

It was my time to speak. I made sure I stayed to the facts. I provided a demonstration of how John pulled my bag away from me, jolting me out of the car, and how I'd tried to get my belongings from him. And yes, I said I'd told him to put a Band-Aid on the scratch.

The judge gave John a chance for rebuttal, but the nonsense coming out of his mouth just made me hold my head down.

The judge apparently felt the same way. She told John this charge was petty and not the proper use of the court system. She ruled that there wasn't sufficient information to grant the restraining order and threw the case out.

By the time I put all my documents in my bag and looked up, John had already left the courtroom. As I walked out, I approached an officer to make sure there was nothing else left for me to do. After seeing John's behavior in the courtroom, the officer was happy to ensure that I knew my rights.

"Make sure you get the document from the clerk that shows the case was dismissed," he said. "And if you want to go back to the house, you can. He can't stop you. That house, the car—it's yours too, so don't let him tell you anything different."

It was interesting to leave the courtroom with officers providing me information about my rights and how I should defend myself, seeing as I was the one who had been served a restraining order in the first place. Each day was becoming clearer as things about John started to unravel.

It was about 3:30 p.m. when I made it back to Cherie's house to rejoin the online training group. I received an instant message from the trainer stating that he had just contacted my manager. He said he was worried we wouldn't have enough time to complete the training today.

My initial thought was that was a bit hasty of him—he and I had already planned to make arrangements to work it out. But I didn't think much of it. We got through the session by five o'clock, at the end of the business day.

A few minutes later, I received another instant message, this time from my manager asking if I could jump on a call with HR.

"Hello—it's Justyne," I announced myself on the conference line.

"Hi, Justyne. I want to talk to you about today," my manager started. "You didn't tell me you were off for the day."

"No, I didn't—because I wasn't off the whole day. I contacted the trainer to let him know I would join the training session later in the day, due to a sudden urgent matter. I said I was prepared to work all night to catch up."

Admittedly, my manager wasn't the first person I had thought to call. Since I'd started that week, I had only communicated with her through a couple of instant messages. The whole week, I had been working under the orientation trainer, so I thought he was the appropriate person to contact.

However, none of this—the communication issue with my manager, the matter with my missing identification documents, and having to miss required training to appear in court—looked good for the first week of a new job. While on the phone with my manager and HR, my computer access was turned off. I was let go from my job. I was heartbroken, but I understood.

Cherie came home with the girls. They brought cake and wine to celebrate the victory at court, my new job, and my new apartment I was planning to move into over the weekend. But then Cherie saw my face.

"I lost the job," I soberly said.

"What? Oh, geez. Girls, go upstairs and change your clothes," Cherie directed. Then she sat down next to me, in complete shock. "What happened?"

I explained the details to Cherie. Like the cheerleader she is, she was ready to write the company a letter to try getting my job back. Within the hour, Cherie completed the letter, I reviewed it, and I sent it to HR and my manager. At this point, though, I didn't expect to receive a response.

"I don't know what to do now. I can't move into the apartment without a job. I'll have to go back to Belleville."

The reality of the situation was setting in. After days on adrenaline, trying to put together the pieces of my life that John attempted to destroy, I was finally out of energy. I didn't have anything left, not even a tear. I went to bed early that night to sleep my thoughts away.

My mom called the next day, asking if I was ready for my move. I replied yes. I didn't think it was good timing to let her know what the situation had come to. It would have just added to her worries about my safety and well-being.

The next morning, I called the apartment leasing manager to cancel my move. I lost my $200 deposit, given the short cancellation time. I decided to spend the day watching movies.

It was Valentine's Day.

The following Sunday, I got dressed for church along with Cherie and the girls. I pulled out a pink blazer from one of the many bags of clothes I had in Cherie's garage.

The significance of going to church wasn't lost on me. John's restraining order had attempted to ban me from the church as well. He was desperate to remove me from every area of his life. He thought he had full control of what happened in my life. But with the restraining order now thrown out, I felt unbothered. I knew John was not in control.

We arrived at church to see John at the door as one of the greeters. I simply gave him a head nod for recognition, then walked through the door he wasn't holding. As usual, I greeted everyone with a smile, then sat with Cherie and the girls during service.

I didn't realize John had left before service ended until Kathy came up to me to ask how I was doing. I hadn't seen her and Ken since they had come to the house that night to help defuse the situation and gather my things.

"Hey, honey—how are you? How did you feel seeing John this morning?" Kathy sweetly asked.

"I felt fine. I didn't feel angry, mad, or anything," I sincerely responded.

It was in that moment I realized I was fine. In spite of everything John had done up to this point to destroy me, I didn't feel any hatred toward him. When I passed him at the door, it was like saying hello to an acquaintance, someone I hardly knew, much less my own husband.

"Wow, that's good. That just shows how pure your heart is," Kathy explained.

Before leaving church, I stopped by to talk to Michelle Peterson. Michelle and her husband, Doug, led the Bible class for married couples that John and I attended.

When she asked me how things were going, I just gave her the basic "fine" response at first. But then I decided to open up and tell her John and I were separated.

"You can stay with us," she instantly said. "I'll talk it over with Doug, but I know it'll be okay."

I didn't even have it in mind to ask about staying with them. I never expected that opening up to Michelle would not only provide me with a home but also a chance to deepen my spiritual relationship and find the strength I needed to move forward. The more I thought about it, the more I realized it was a good idea to be around a married couple with a family during this time. It would help me strengthen my faith in wanting my marriage to be fixed. Michelle and Doug were good at counseling couples during hard times.

After church, Cherie and I headed out to do some shopping. Then I received an email from John.

Subject: Moving Forward

Good day, Justyne—
This situation is much worse than I—than we—want it to be. I'm sorry for my role in it. Let's talk to clear things up to avoid any uncertainties. What can we do to move forward?
John

I didn't know what to think about the email. I must have read it fifty times, trying to decode what John meant about "avoid any uncertainties." And why did he asked me, "What can we do to move forward?"

Cherie maybe wasn't the right person to guide me through this dilemma. When I read her the email, her first words were, "Chile, please—don't respond to it. Let him wait. Maybe tomorrow you can reply."

I just shook my head and smiled. My natural reaction was to respond right away to acknowledge the email and to apologize too. I wasn't good at this, however. My niceness hadn't served me very well up to this point. Then I wondered if John would have sent this email if the judge had ruled in his favor to enforce the restraining order.

For the rest of the day, I contemplated whether I should respond. I didn't reply until very late, just before going to bed. I decided to keep it short, because I didn't understand where John was coming from.

Subject: Re: Moving Forward

Good night, John—
Yes, I agree we do need to have a discussion. Let me know when you are available. I think the first thing we should do moving forward is to get on amicable terms.
Take care,
Justyne

The next few days, I was busy looking for another job and packing my things to go stay with Michelle and Doug. I was so grateful that Cherie and her girls had opened their two-bedroom home when I needed it the most, but I was happy not to burden them any longer.

Michelle planned to help me move on Wednesday. It worked out perfectly, seeing as John and I had scheduled a time to talk over the phone on Thursday. I had a day to get settled and get prepared for my conversation with John.

Just before my call on Thursday, I wrote out what I wanted to say so I wouldn't go off script. Michelle prayed for me before my call to give me some encouragement and wisdom.

I took a seat on the couch and dialed John's number. The phone rang to voice mail, even though I was calling at our scheduled time. I sent John an email to let him know I had called, but I got no reply. He eventually called back shortly after.

"Hi," he said.

"Hi," I replied.

"So, let me say this first," John blurted. "Be careful what you are saying about me to other people. Second, I need the files for the restaurant. I will need this in order for us to get on amicable terms."

I was taken aback by John's sharpness. I didn't know what to say. I thought the conversation would have started at a more civil place, more along the lines of "I'm sorry. Let's try to fix this." But it was much further away from that. There was at least a thirty-second pause before I said anything.

"I will send you the files you need. But we also need to talk about the outstanding loan for the business," I finally said.

Very quickly, John wouldn't let me say anything more. He kept going on about what he needed for the restaurant. He wasn't ready to deal with the real issues of how our marriage had gotten to this point. Talking about the restaurant was the safest thing he could manage. The conversation escalated into an argument, and it no longer served a purpose. When we got off the phone, I emailed John all the files he'd asked for.

Over the next few weeks, John emailed me to request other things he wanted. He even asked for my restaurant work shirt and the sample shirt I got from the designer. I put everything in a plastic bag and left it at Cherie's house for him to pick up.

9

WHEN WE GOT MARRIED

September to December 2011

On the plane ride back from Washington, I called my mom to let her know John had proposed and we were engaged to be married. She didn't believe it at first. John had already approached my parents to ask for my hand in marriage, so they were expecting it—just not so soon.

Later that day, I spoke to John's mom. She seemed upset and insinuated that I had lied to her when I saw her in August. She suggested that John and I were already engaged at that time but just didn't tell her about it. Once I explained that John had just now proposed on the trip, she understood.

I got back home to Belleville, excited to share the news with the rest of my family and friends as well as to start planning the wedding, which was three months away. John and I already had the December 12 date in mind, and I really wanted to stick to it. That was partly why I had been so anxious for him to propose; I'd wanted to give our family and friends enough time to plan to attend.

The process of planning the wedding was quite smooth. We decided to have the wedding in Houston because it was winter in Belleville. Plus, I figured it would be easier for people to travel to south Texas than to Canada if they didn't have their passports.

We also decided that I would move to Houston. I was already on a work visa. It would be an easier transition for me to obtain permanent residency in the United States than for John to move to Belleville, find another job, and go through the lengthy process of getting cleared to work in Canada.

There were moments when John and I had disagreements, but we were able to work through them. I chose a wedding dress quite quickly to ensure it would be delivered in time. I called John to share my excitement, but he didn't sound too enthused. Actually, it had nothing to do with my buying a dress. He was upset because he had just found out a good friend couldn't make the wedding.

Because of the short time frame, we realized some invitees wouldn't be able to attend. But we also hoped that those who really wanted to be there would be there to support our union together. John wanted his friend to be one of his groomsmen, but his friend wasn't able to leave his work in Dubai. It was a visa issue his friend couldn't do anything about, but John continued to sound sober as we talked over the phone. I didn't know what else to say to make him feel better. We eventually ended the call, and I sat on the couch no longer excited about my wedding dress.

In the weeks leading up to the wedding, I started to move my things to Houston in between my work travel trips. While packing my clothes in suitcases, I remember thinking, *What the heck am I doing?* It felt so unreal.

I thought about all the years I'd shared with Michael, thinking that one day we would be together. And now I was packing to move to Houston to marry someone I'd been dating for only the past year.

But John's steadfast pursuit of me and follow-through with the proposal made me believe this was meant to be. The way we'd reconnected two years after the Las Vegas conference, after Michael was completely out of my life, also made me believe the timing was meant to be. If we had started dating the first time we'd met in Las Vegas, I don't think the relationship would have lasted. Neither of us were ready at that time.

As I packed my suitcase, I felt God's grace ushering me into this new chapter of my life. I was happy about it; this was what I wanted.

During a visit to Houston, John arranged for me to meet his daughter, Josephine. We drove an hour and a half to pick her up to take her to the movies. When we pulled up to the driveway, Josephine ran out and opened the back door to get into the car. She was so happy to see her daddy that she was smiling ear to ear.

"Hi, Josephine. This is Justyne. Say hi," John greeted and instructed his daughter.

"Hi," Josephine replied innocently as she put on her seat belt.

We arrived at the theater to see a movie of Josephine's choice. I watched her cling onto him with such possession. I think she was nervous I was around. When we got inside, Josephine sat between us.

"Are you my dad's girlfriend?" Josephine turned to me and asked.

"What did your dad say?" I asked back, wanting to make sure I didn't say something John didn't want to me say.

"He said you were," Josephine replied.

"Okay, then. Yes, I am."

Apparently, this was the first time John had told Josephine I even existed. I didn't bother asking when he would tell his daughter we were getting married.

Both Josephine and Nicole, his ex-wife, were very surprised when John eventually told them he was getting married in just a few weeks. John purposely kept them in the dark about his life. According to him, it was because of his ex-wife's bad intentions. Despite the shock, Josephine was very excited about the news and the upcoming wedding.

Less than a month until our wedding day, I started to feel John was not communicating well. I was planning a wedding while also moving into John's home—two major events happening at the same time. Yet John didn't seem to be making the move any easier. He left me little room for my things. The closet was full, and I had to leave the remaining clothes and shoes in my luggage, which meant I had less luggage to take back and forth with each trip. I had told him we needed a dresser for me, but he still hadn't bought one.

Perhaps he didn't realize how big of a transition I was making for us to be together. I decided to write him a lengthy email to express how I felt. Given our long distance, we still often dealt with issues through email or phone. We didn't spend enough time dealing with issues face-to-face. Later that day, I received a response from John.

Subject: Re: Express Yourself

Thank you for your note. I didn't realize some of your clothes were still in the suitcases. As I said, I'm watching for that dresser to go on sale this weekend. Sorry.
John

Few words from John was something I had to get used to. Likewise, many words from me was something he had to get used to. It was definitely an area we both needed to work on.

On my last trip to Houston, I'd planned to stay until the wedding day. I knew by this time John had bought the dresser, but I began to doubt whether he had put it together. When I asked him about the dresser, he just smiled. I shook my head, preparing myself to put the dresser together that evening. But when I took my bags into the bedroom, I was pleasantly surprised to see the dresser put up. It was simple moments like these that reminded me John cared about me.

The wedding was two weeks away. John and I got into a discussion about where each of us would get ready the day of the wedding. I preferred to get dressed at the house because of the hair and makeup activities for me and the bridal party. But John also wanted to get ready at the house. I didn't understand why—I guess because it was his house.

We argued about this for a while until we concluded that I and the bridal party would get dressed upstairs, and he and his groomsmen would get dressed downstairs, then go to his friend's house to take pictures.

The night before the wedding, we completed the rehearsal, then got back home and just lay in bed. The silence between us was awkward. It was as if we didn't have words to express to each other, but we were getting married the next day, so we had to say something. John started to say the Lord's Prayer. We prayed together and held each other's hand until we fell asleep.

I woke up at six in the morning to meet my girlfriends at the hair salon. Along the way, I went to the hotel where John's family was staying to pick up Josephine. At the salon, I noticed the sad look on her face. I chose not to ask too many questions. She had been excited about the wedding when she first heard the news. Now I had a feeling she was sad because she wasn't in the wedding party. Although I had suggested to John that we make Josephine a flower girl, he'd decided not to. Josephine took it especially hard. I believe it initiated a big strain in their relationship.

Everyone was done by noon. I had enough time to bring Josephine back to the hotel and run additional errands before heading back to the house to do my makeup and get dressed for the wedding at four that afternoon. As soon as I got to the house, I ran upstairs so John wouldn't see me.

I heard John's voice downstairs, then more voices as his groomsmen started to gather. John's sister Veronica was one of my bridesmaids, but she knew most of his friends, so she spent most of her time downstairs while the rest of the bridesmaids were upstairs getting ready. When the guys left, I could tell Veronica felt uncomfortable back with us ladies. She made a comment about having no one to talk to. I guess she felt comfortable only with people she knew.

The limo arrived to pick up the bridesmaids. We had enough time to take pictures and record video messages. I was truly elated—I was marrying John, a man who was completely in love with me and whom I wanted to be with.

The wedding ceremony was beautiful. My cousin who traveled from Philadelphia told me it reminded her of something in the movies.

After the ceremony, we headed to the park to take pictures before going to the reception venue. The limo driver dropped off the bridal party, then was nice enough to take John and me on a private ride through the city. I expected John to be all over me, but oddly, he wasn't. He was more concerned about how tired he was than the private time we had with each other in that moment. I just sat there as John slumped his head on my shoulder and took a quick nap.

When we arrived at the reception venue, I looked for my mom so she could help me bustle the train on my dress. The only reason I'd paid extra money for the seamstress to put in the hooks and eyes for the bustle was because my mom assured me she'd remember how to do it. Well, when the moment arrived, my mother didn't remember a thing. I was so upset and disappointed. No one could find the hooks and eyes to properly bustle it up.

John came to find out what was wrong. He decided to create his own "hooks" by ripping small holes to pin up the dress. John felt good that he had a solution to the problem. It was cute.

By the time the reception got on its way, I'd forgotten how upset I had gotten over the dress. The reception was held in one of the tallest buildings in Houston, so guests had a great view of the city landscape. We didn't have to invest in too many decorations, as the dining room had its own elegant ambiance with dangling chandeliers. The reception went on until 11:00 p.m.

John and I got a chance to give our thank-you speech to our guests before the evening ended. I concluded my speech by letting John know how happy I was to be his wife and that I loved him dearly. However, in his speech, he just thanked our family and friends for coming out. He didn't say "I love you" at any time during his speech. I noticed. Perhaps he was nervous.

We got a ride home from John's best man, Peter. John and I spent our wedding night back at the house, seeing as we were leaving to go on our honeymoon in a couple of days. We were both exhausted from the long day, not to mention the long days leading up to the wedding.

I asked John to help me zip down my dress, and he was happy to oblige. I got out of the dress and took a shower so I could put on the white lingerie I'd been saving for many years, waiting for this moment—this moment that was very special to me, to us both.

I walked out of the bathroom in beautiful white lingerie sequins. John just walked by, heading right out of the room.

"Hey, do you like this?" I asked him when he returned.

"Oh yes. It looks nice," he responded.

I walked over to the bed, feeling a little insecure. As we lay in the bed, the anticipation of my husband being excited to make love to his wife for the first time was quickly dismissed when John fell asleep.

Then in the middle of the night, John woke up, turned toward me, and started to kiss me. We ended up consummating the marriage. It felt like a cheap thrill. There was nothing romantic or affectionate about the moment. I had to encourage myself in my mind so I wouldn't feel hurt and unloved.

The next morning, John left the house, barely saying anything to me. As I went into the bathroom to fix my hair, I wondered what I had done to make John act so distant. I felt extremely unwanted and unloved during the first twenty-four hours of our marriage—and it continued throughout our five-day honeymoon in Aruba.

John was ready to leave that first night. I hadn't experienced this type of disconnection with anyone before. It was like pulling teeth to have a flowing conversation. John just wanted to sleep during the entire honeymoon. I couldn't understand how a husband could treat his wife in such an unloving way.

We did have some moments of fun while sightseeing, going to the beach, and going to dinner. But they were interrupted by insensitive comments such as "Are you going to eat that?" Suddenly my weight was a concern, and I became self-conscious about it.

By the last day, we were both ready to go home. Back in Texas at the airport, we had to wait curbside for the shuttle bus to take us to the parking lot to pick up our car. I was still trying to get John to be more affectionate, so I moved close to him and hugged him up a bit. He gave me this look wondering what I was doing, and he took steps away from me in the other direction. My mind started to go in all kinds of directions.

We stopped at John's sister's house, where his parents were staying, to give them a few things we bought on our honeymoon. It was great to see his parents again and have a quick chat before heading home.

It was my turn to drive, and about thirty minutes into the ride, I noticed from the corner of my eye John putting something in his mouth.

"What are you eating?" I asked, surprised he didn't offer me anything.

"Nothing," he replied.

"What? I saw you pull something out and eat it," I said, convinced of what I saw.

"It's nothing. It's just a piece of bread," he said as if nothing were wrong.

"Where did you get that? Why didn't you offer me a piece?" I asked, now visibly upset.

"It's carbs—I thought you were going to stay away from them."

"I don't remember saying that. At least you could have offered me a piece. We're both in the car, and we haven't eaten yet." I was pissed.

All John said was, "Hey, you better slow down."

I had gotten the car up to one hundred miles per hour without even noticing.

John knew I was very upset, yet he didn't say anything else to me. I kept quiet as well.

When we got home, I helped unload the car, then went upstairs to watch television in the guest room. John didn't seem to mind the negative energy between us. I stayed upstairs the whole night, and John stayed downstairs. Our first night back from our honeymoon was spent in separate rooms.

In the morning, I came downstairs to see John on the couch opening the wedding gifts and cards.

"What are you doing?" I exclaimed. "Did you open our wedding gifts?" I asked, already knowing the answer.

"You weren't here. I only opened the ones from my family and friends," John said as he opened another envelope.

I started to cry. I couldn't believe John was this selfish and inconsiderate to not realize that opening the wedding gifts was a moment we should experience together. Needless to say, this only added to my existing hurt. The lack of an apology just made it worse.

The next couple of days remained the same. Hurt and upset by John's insensitivity, I had nothing to say. And John didn't talk to me because I wasn't talking to him.

It was now Sunday, three days since our honeymoon, and we were still sleeping in separate rooms. I heard John get ready for church. He texted me, asking if I was going to church. I responded no. I heard the door close as he left the house to go to church anyway.

Texting became our only form of communication, and even that was strained. I received another text later that day, telling me he had invited friends over for dinner. He asked if I would still isolate myself. I replied that it wasn't a good idea to have his friends over while things were unresolved between us. His reply just said what time his friends would arrive.

I eventually came downstairs to join the dinner, but only because one of his friends came upstairs to get me. But I had very little to say. I sat the at dinner table silent as if I were watching a movie. It further upset me that John could be jovial and chatty around his friends and ignore that things weren't right between us.

After John's friends left, I went back upstairs. John texted to let me know he was giving me five minutes to come downstairs to talk about what was wrong. I wondered why he was telling *me* to come to *him*. I texted to let him know I wasn't coming downstairs.

Moments later, John blazed into the room as if he had been forced to do something he didn't want to do.

"Now what is your problem?"

I was sitting on the edge of the bed, looking out the window, crying, wishing I were back in Belleville. I wanted to go back home. I didn't know what I had gotten myself into by marrying John. I didn't want to be there anymore. I didn't want to be with John. He wasn't my friend or someone I thought loved me.

"So, are you going to speak? What's your problem?" John continued.

I started to outline the chain of events.

"On our honeymoon, you wanted to leave after the first day. Then you started making comments about my size, and you rudely hid food from me because you didn't want me to eat. When we got home, you ignored the fact I was upset. You didn't even talk to me. We didn't sleep in the same bed on our first night home together, and that seemed okay to you. Then in the morning, I walked downstairs to find you opening the wedding gifts without me. And you carried on throughout the days, ignoring that things weren't right between us. Are you *serious*?"

The more I talked, the more I cried, realizing how hurt I was.

John had no empathy. "Tears do nothing to me." Then out of nowhere, he added, "Even my little nephew called to see how I was doing. He cares a lot about his uncle and is concerned. With my family, if they see that their son, uncle, brother is not happy, they will not like you. Since my cousin's death, we're more concerned about each other."

I sat there in total confusion, trying to understand what John was saying. His cousin, who grew up with him and his family like a brother, died suddenly in a car accident six years earlier; it devastated the family. John was very close to his cousin and looked up to him. He even told me the last time he'd cried was at his funeral. John was the youngest of five siblings: three sisters and two brothers. I understood how the death brought the family closer. However, I didn't understand the impact it would have on our marriage.

"The kids made a comment about how you didn't interact with them much during the wedding," he continued.

"What are you talking about?" I said, finally seizing a chance to speak. "There were so many things going on during the wedding. The kids helped me put together the cake boxes. What was the problem with that?"

At that time, I didn't realize what was happening—John was doing everything and anything to make sure he didn't look at fault.

By the end of the conversation, John let me know it was my decision to stay upstairs or go downstairs. Although hesitant and uncomfortable, I decided to go downstairs to join my husband in our bedroom.

PART II

OUR MARRIAGE

10

FIRST YEAR

December 2011 to December 2012

Before we knew, it was Christmas; we had been married two weeks. I was looking forward to celebrating our first Christmas as a married couple. Although the marriage hadn't started on the right foot, it was still early enough to change things around.

John and I woke up early Sunday morning to get ready for church. John had attended this church for several years, was very active in the ministry activities, and knew many members. Back in Belleville, I had attended a church I loved very much. I even did some research to find a similar church in Houston with the same teaching and structure. But given John's attachment to the church he attended, he wasn't too enthused about finding somewhere else to go. I didn't push it any further and became a member at the church he attended.

After service, we met up with a few other members in the parking lot for a quick chat. As we gathered in a circle talking back and forth, John decided to invite the members to our house after the New Year's Eve service. I stood there listening to John make plans with people I had just met, without asking me one question.

When we got into the car, I turned to John. "So, what are we doing for New Year's Eve?"

John looked at me puzzled. "What? Is something wrong?"

"Well, you didn't talk to me before inviting people over," I responded.

John got defensive. "So? You were there when I brought it up. You could have said something."

"First off, I don't know these people," I assertively said. "Second, when people started talking about New Year's Eve, you could have said, 'Let Justyne and me see what we have planned and get back to you,' rather than making the plan without talking to me."

John didn't like my response very much. He suddenly got very cold with me. He continued to drive without saying a word. This got me even more upset.

We arrived at John's friend's house so John could look at the landscaping in the backyard to provide recommendations. John worked in construction but had a passion for farming, so he was familiar with gardening and landscaping. I was so upset with John ignoring me that I slammed the car door when I got out. This made John finally say something to me.

"Don't slam the car door!"

Mr. Franklin, John's friend, walked up to us. "Hey, John! How are you doing? Look at your beautiful wife! You must tell her that every day. You've got to take care of her!"

Mr. Franklin was a member of the church and took quite a liking to me. His words were timelier than he realized.

John quickly said hello and ignored everything else Mr. Franklin said.

It took about fifteen minutes for John to assess Mr. Franklin's yard to determine what he needed to do to achieve the landscaping he wanted. We got back in the car to drive home. I decided I wouldn't say anything. Ten minutes into the car ride, John decided to speak to me.

"Before you, I would always have my friends over and entertain. That won't change because we're married. I should be able to continue to do this with you."

"I'm used to having friends over and entertaining as well. But my point was that it should be something we decide *together*. You don't know if I wanted to do something special with just the two of us for our first New Year's together."

"Well, do you have anything planned?" John asked.

"No, but—"

John cut me off once he heard what he wanted to hear.

I took a deep breath, paused, and decided not to say anything else. I knew in that moment there was nothing I could say that would make John understand how his actions and response had affected me. I didn't think he cared.

With everything that had happened since getting married, I started to write a journal to help me with my thoughts and feelings.

December 26, 2011

Dear God,
I'm married now and I've moved to Houston, but I believe you already know this. I'm not sure how I'm supposed to feel or what other newlyweds feel, but I don't feel happy. I've married a man who doesn't know how to love. I don't even want to talk to friends because they will ask about my honeymoon, and I don't have much to say. My husband hardly touched me, had very little to say to me, and wanted to go home the first day.

I don't know how to navigate around this—a man who doesn't know how to show love, affection, respect, and friendliness. He is so uptight and wrapped up in himself. Why get married if you don't know how to be around someone? He comes in the house and doesn't even speak. I have to go to him and speak in order to start a conversation. I don't have good thoughts about the personality of the man I've married. How do you love someone who doesn't love you back? He doesn't even say "I love you." How can a woman be in a relationship with someone like this? I knew he wasn't the most affectionate

*guy, but this is definitely a lot worse than I'd thought. I
feel like a stranger, isolated, alone, and an inconvenience.
Please, Lord, show me how to be the person you need
me to be to turn this situation around. Help me say
what needs to be said in the right way and time. Please
strengthen my heart so that I'm not easily offended by
the things John does and doesn't do. Help me find solid
ground, so I can feel comfortable.*

  *Anyway, I should go now. Trying to think of better
things and keep focus.*

Work in progress,
Justyne

My first holidays with John was a roller coaster of emotions. I found
myself trying each day to figure out how John felt about me and even
how I felt about him. I was having thoughts and feelings I didn't
think were normal for a newlywed, so I found myself very torn. I was
still trying to adjust to living in John's house and making it feel like
my own, but even that was challenging. John limited what I could
and couldn't do. He didn't want me to spend a lot of time and money
doing much to the house.

  One day I was sitting on the couch, and John mentioned that I
hadn't cleaned the house since I'd been there. He specifically pointed
out that the television stand had accumulated dust. I honestly hadn't
even noticed the television stand needed to be cleaned because I
still felt like a guest in the house. When you're a guest in someone
else's home, you don't start cleaning. It was as if I were just there
temporarily; it hadn't registered that John's house was my house too.

  Ideally, it would have been nice if John and I had gotten a new
home together. But given the timing, we didn't have that option. John
and I spoke about looking into finding a new home within a couple
of years. In the meantime, I worked on minor projects to incorporate
my personal touches in the house.

One night, I was in the bathroom and noticed I didn't have a drawer for my things. That made me sad. I went into the living room and sat on the couch. All my feelings rushed through me, and I started to cry, thinking of being somewhere else, somewhere I felt loved and wanted.

I think John felt my sadness this time. Later that evening, he pulled out the bottom drawer in the bathroom to show me he had cleared it out to make room for my things—if I needed, he added.

December 27, 2011

Dear God,
I'm trying to stay above what I'm experiencing until I find solid ground. I had a moment in which I wanted to make a point but missed it. There was this green bar of soap I brought from Belleville that John opened. I thought he was using it to bathe, so I also used it. I noticed the soap always moved, until one day I didn't see it anymore. I later found out that John had hid the soap in a ziplock bag in the drawer. He didn't say a word. Today I asked him what happened to the green bar of soap. He said he washes his face with it. Apparently, he didn't want me to bathe with the same soap he used for his face. What I wanted to say but didn't was, why didn't you say that from the beginning instead of hiding the soap? Oh, geez. Please, Lord, help me trust that John will learn to communicate soon. Wow, communication is the bloodline of a relationship, especially in a marriage, but this guy doesn't even know how to open his mouth. I truly pray for him and look forward to the day when I can rejoice about it! Until then, patience is all I have, and even though I can't talk to my husband, at least I can write.
On top of that, I bought some things for the house but got no comment. I had to ask him if he liked what

I'd bought. It doesn't feel like home yet. I think it will feel like home when I can change something without telling John or when he won't move something back after I've already changed it. Everything I thought I would feel, I don't feel. I believe John is trying. Please, Lord, help me be a support to him. God gives me strength.

Thank you,
Justyne

It was New Year's Eve. John and I spent the day at home. Before we headed to evening church service, I started pulling things out in the kitchen to prepare for the gathering happening later that night. I wanted to show John my support. I didn't know what John had in mind for the party, and when I asked, he didn't give much of a clear response. Given my structured and organized approach to things, this had me feeling completely uncomfortable. I had no direction or plan for this party we would be hosting. But most of all, I felt like a stranger in what was supposed to be my home.

After church service, John and I rushed back home so we could start preparing food for our guests. As soon as we opened the door, John headed straight for the kitchen.

"John, you still have your shoes on," I mentioned.

"Yes, I know," he responded.

"Can you take them off?"

My biggest pet peeve was someone wearing shoes in the house. I could never understand how people could wear the same shoes inside that they wear outside. It disturbed me to think about all the bugs, dirt, and bodily fluids that could be tracked inside the house.

John waited a few minutes until he finally decided to oblige my request.

I looked in the kitchen, and John had his hands involved in every aspect of the food preparation. There was no room for me to assist. I didn't know how to help or even how to find my place in the kitchen.

Finally, I grabbed John's hand and gave him a kiss. "Let's do this together."

He smiled, and that seemed to change the direction of things for a bit. But in the end, John simply took over in the kitchen and gave me the sense that he didn't want my help.

The doorbell rang. Our first guests arrived. Within ten minutes, everyone had arrived. Most of the folks were church members who were close friends with John.

Suddenly, people were helping themselves in the kitchen, incorporating their touches to the food. The guests were more comfortable in the kitchen than I was. John seemed happy to have their help, and he started showing off his cooking skills to add to the fun.

Soon John declared it was time to eat, even though the fish I was cooking wasn't ready yet. The guests stepped up to set the table and bring out the food. John took the pot of grits from the stove and put it right on the dinner table.

All I could think was, *Who does that? Who puts a pot on the table at a dinner party? What about serving dishes and plates?* I just stood there, exasperated and insecure. I had no control of what was going on around me. It disturbed me tremendously.

Even though the party was all John's idea, I still wanted to make a good impression with his friends. As the woman of the house, I wanted to add my style and help set the tone for how we entertained as a married couple. But instead, this party only showed how John did things on his own.

For the rest of the evening, I remained quiet. The ladies tried to engage in small talk with me, but I was too overwhelmed to have a conversation. It was obvious that I wasn't feeling the evening.

It just wasn't the right time for us to entertain guests; John and I first had to find our own rhythm together. By this time in our marriage, we'd returned from a rocky honeymoon, slept in separate rooms for the first four days in our home, had two major arguments that left us not talking to each other for days, struggled with my attempts to make the house my home, and now had a tension-filled dinner party. And it was only week three. If John had considered everything we'd been through, perhaps he would have realized we needed to focus on being a couple before hosting parties.

Guests started leaving earlier than expected. While we were in the kitchen, I saw a few people heading for the door.

"Aren't you going to see your friends out?" I asked John.

"Oh, so they're only 'my' friends?" he sarcastically responded.

I was confused by his reaction. They truly were his friends more than mine. I had just met them. Apparently, he assumed I would automatically embrace the situation.

When everyone left, John was so upset that he left everything in the kitchen and went straight to bed. He didn't want to talk to me.

I went into the bedroom and slipped into the bed. John's back was turned to me.

"John, we shouldn't go to bed angry. We should try to talk about it," I said.

"Well, we'll just have to go to bed angry tonight," he replied.

Although it was a hot day in Texas, the bed was so cold that I grabbed a blanket to cover myself up.

The next few days got a little better. One night, John brought home a cheese platter and set it on the dining table.

"Hey, I bought this for us to eat tonight." John sat in the chair, waiting for me to join him.

I sat at the table. "Oh, this is nice. Thank you," I replied, trying not to say too much.

"How are you feeling?" John asked.

"I'm okay. I guess."

"What's wrong?"

"I don't think things have been going well, and I don't know how you feel."

John held his head down to take a breath and looked back at me. "I agree. I think we've been misunderstanding each other. We're probably moving too fast into what we think marriage should be. I think we should use tonight to start over again," John concluded.

Other times, we ignored each other when we were upset. But this time, we actually talked about how we felt and what had happened on New Year's Eve. It was a good start, yet John was reluctant to take the conversation deeper.

I started to look at our marriage and even myself differently after that conversation. It was hard sometimes to think positively about our situation, but I needed to try. I believed John truly wanted a happy life with me. I needed to try hard to not view and receive his actions and words in a negative way. I was thankful for the revelation I'd received in that conversation with John. I hoped that things would begin to change.

In January, I went back to work. I started traveling to Detroit Monday through Thursday every week. Although I was away from John, I felt a lot better than I did when I was at the house. It was one thing to feel alone when traveling. But to feel alone when you're in your own home with your own husband was really not a good feeling. One month into our marriage, I was still trying to understand how I felt about everything, trying to understand how my husband loved me, trying to understand how to create my own happiness that wasn't in isolation of my marriage.

When I was home, I began to get self-conscious about my weight. John told me he preferred me to be a size 2, and he told me how I should work toward that goal. I'd never had the desire to be a size 2, not even wished for it. I'd been on the "forever workout plan" my whole adult life, thriving and learning to be comfortable with my weight. And up to that point, I had been comfortable with it. But now it didn't seem good enough.

One Sunday afternoon, I went grocery shopping and saw Ben & Jerry's ice cream on sale—two for five dollars. I'd never had Ben & Jerry's, so I was excited to try it. When I got home, I put the ice cream in the freezer and planned to enjoy it when I returned home from my work travel later that week.

Thursday night on my way home from the airport, all I could think about was putting on my cozy pajamas and eating a big scoop of ice cream. John was working the night shift, so he wasn't home. Once home, I went into the kitchen to take out the ice cream, but to my surprise, it was nowhere to be found. I checked all the shelves in the freezer, and there was no ice cream. I didn't know what had happened. I decided to call John.

"Hey, John—um, I'm in the freezer looking for the Ben & Jerry's ice cream I bought on Sunday. Do you know where it is?"

"Yes, I do," John slowly replied.

"Okay, where is it?" I asked, bewildered.

"It's at the store."

"At the store? What do you mean?"

"I returned it."

"You *what*?" I burst out. "You returned the ice cream I bought? Why did you do that?"

"You said you're trying to lose weight, and eating ice cream isn't going to help that, so I took it back."

"Are you kidding me? You had no right to do that."

"So, you're upset about not having ice cream?" John flippantly asked.

I was so insulted by John's actions that I quickly ended the conversation and hung up. The fact that John thought returning the ice cream was just and helpful was disturbing. I couldn't believe he would do such a thing.

The magnitude of my moving to Houston became a reality one day. I suddenly realized that I had totally submerged myself into John's life. I had left everything and everyone I knew behind. I had to try hard to remember who I was and who my friends and family were back home, the people who cared for and loved me. I was waiting for the person I knew I was to show up, but that person was scared and had retreated into a shell.

Hoping to reach out more to my new community, I volunteered to assist our church fellowship group with plans for a Valentine's Day couples' dinner. I enjoyed having something to work on while John was working on his business plan for a restaurant he wanted to open.

A few days before the Valentine's Day dinner, John and I got into an argument and didn't talk to each other for days. I was so used to this treatment that I found strength in going about my days as usual.

The dinner was on Saturday evening, and John had been gone for most of the day. I snacked on food throughout the day but didn't cook any meals. John was so picky—I didn't know what to cook to make him satisfied. Later that afternoon, John came home with food from McDonald's, and he ate in the living room. I could tell he was unhappy, but he didn't say anything.

"What time do we have to leave tonight?" John finally asked from the couch.

"Well, we have to be at the Village Manor by seven o'clock. How long will it take us to get there?"

"We'll be fine if we leave by six thirty," he replied.

"Okay, great!" I said cheerfully. "Oh, don't forget we have to wear black and red."

These interactions showed me he didn't care much about the situation, so I made sure I took care of myself. I decided to remain happy and unbothered to keep things moving. I went upstairs to get ready in that bathroom instead of the one in our bedroom.

An hour later, I received a text from John:

> Hey there. Let's talk before we head out for dinner.

I went downstairs.

The conversation started with John pointing out how I didn't cook for him and how he had to go out to buy food, which he hardly ever did. He then continued with how I wasn't doing things around the house and how we weren't getting along.

I tried to wrap my mind around everything John said, but his lack of self-awareness of how he had contributed to the issues was alarming. I couldn't even understand what kind of conversation I was having.

"Well, we could just get a divorce and go our separate ways," I abruptly suggested.

At this point, I was emotionally uninvested and emptied. I didn't care which direction our marriage went.

"It's been over three months, so it's too late to get an annulment," John responded as if he had already researched it.

There were minutes of silence before another word was spoken.

"Okay. So what else can we do?" I asked to break the silence.

"We can continue to work through things until it gets better."

I didn't know what John meant by that. Up to that moment, he had never seemed willing to confront our issues.

"We can go to counseling . . ." I suggested.

"Ah . . . no. I don't think we need that right now. We'll just continue to pray and work on things," John concluded.

"Okay." I didn't persist. I went back upstairs to finish getting ready. The evening ended with a fun dinner with our church fellowship group and a quiet drive back home.

The next few months felt like a tug-of-war, with John and me on opposite sides, pulling the other in our own direction. We focused more on our individual endeavors than on building our marriage. We had little quality time together. I was home only on weekends, when John was juggling his own work schedule and errands.

In moments when I felt I couldn't talk to John, I would write him emails to express everything on my heart. One email came after feeling a strong disconnection between us and needing to release my thoughts.

Subject: Express Yourself

Hey, sweetheart—

I'm writing this letter to "air out" what's in my head! I love you—I really do love you—and I just want to focus on that. So, I hope by writing down what's in my head, it will be my way of letting this go so that I (we) can move on. It's important that we understand each other, and sometimes I feel I may not verbally express myself in the way I want to.

Okay, so here it goes . . .

I had an aha moment the other night, when we revealed the deep thoughts/feelings we harbored about each other, in that you feel I'm not totally committed and I feel your love is not very deep for me. It made me realize we have protective walls up. One feeling is a reaction and/or result to another feeling, and the cycle continues.

I believe the lack of trust in our relationship is based out of fear. That's different from a lack of trust based out of betrayal or disrespect. This makes me want to focus on breaking down my "wall" by identifying what caused it to be built in the first place. I admit that my defense and protective walls are up as well as my fears—but I don't want them to be there anymore. I want to get to a place of full trust and vulnerability with you . . . so I start my journey now!

I first have to admit I've developed a belief in my mind that you don't "really" love me. I say this because I feel your love toward me is conditional to the way I look (my size), how I cook, how I keep the house, and basically anything that shapes your fundamental views on the role of a woman/wife. I suppose you can say I think I'm not meeting your expectations, therefore I do not feel genuine love from you. It actually makes me feel like this is an arranged marriage with a checklist. This is the basis of my reaction toward you. This may sound crazy, but this is my wall.

I want to hear you say I'm beautiful . . . you love the way I look . . . you think I'm sexy . . . you love me completely . . . I'm the only woman for you. I want to hear you edify my spirit and soul. This is what motivates me.

In contrast, to hear you tell me what things I could do to make my body look "better" and what size you prefer me to be doesn't motivate me. It causes me to be resistant, resentful, defensive, and it just doesn't make me feel good. This is a real issue for me; I just hope you understand. I want to draw nearer to you, knowing I will be accepted for the way I am. I don't want to live a life in fear of my husband not accepting me. We haven't been married for six months yet, and you've already expressed what I could work on physically to be more attractive to you.

I really do hope I can let this go now. If anything else comes to my mind, I'll just email it to you, because just like you, I don't want to talk about this anymore! We keep saying the same things, and I don't think our respective views on this will change. You will continue to think it's perfectly fine for a husband to specify how he wants his wife to look, and I will continue to think it's not appropriate. I don't think it's wrong for you to have desires or preferences; my disagreement is how you have imposed them on me, given that you married me the way I am (well, actually twelve pounds more).

I love you very much as my husband. I appreciate what you have done and are doing in my life by ensuring that I (we) live a healthy lifestyle. That alone motivates me to continue to want to be desirable to you.

Good night!

Justyne

Three hours later, while working the night shift, John responded. He started with Hebrews 11:6: "But without faith it is impossible to please Him, for he who comes to God must believe that He is, and that He is a rewarder of those who diligently seek Him."

John continued to express how action oriented he was and how that may have played a role in his reaction toward me. He said he was disappointed that I didn't want to exercise around him or with him.

I paused at this.

John further explained how our gracious God wants us to show that we are diligently working toward pleasing Him and seeking Him. But he did clarify that he doesn't expect a perfect wife.

I paused again.

John ended by letting me know he was there for me. He said he looked forward to working and praying together to release those barriers between us. He concluded with "I got your back. I love you, Justyne Black!"

I felt better knowing I had poured out my heart to John. Now I had to wait and see if he had truly heard me and if he wanted to show a different side of himself that would allow us to develop a deeper relationship.

In April, John and I planned a trip to California to visit his friend. While still traveling for work, I tried to coordinate with John so we could go online together to reserve our seats next to each other on the plane. When I called John, however, he told me he'd already reserved his own seat. I looked, but there were no seats open near him.

I was obviously disappointed. It was a five-hour flight, and I wanted to sit with my husband. Rather than apologizing, John got upset that I was upset about it.

The day of the trip, I flew from my work location to Phoenix, where John's flight was connecting. John was already seated when I boarded the plane. He didn't say a word as I walked past his row to the back of the plane, where I was seated.

John's birthday was approaching. I enjoy birthdays and always take time to celebrate regardless of what else is happening. I wanted to make this birthday special for John because my last attempt didn't go as well as I had hoped.

When John's birthday came around last time, we were still dating long distance, and I couldn't be there in person to celebrate with him. So, I arranged to have a package of chocolates sent with a personalized message: "Happy birthday, my sweetheart. No distance can separate how I feel about you. You are the strength, protection, and love that fills my heart completely."

I called John at work during the day. Without giving away the surprise, I wanted to see if he had received the chocolates that morning at home. He didn't mention them, so I assumed they would be waiting for him after work.

But then John happened to mention it was raining. I got nervous, thinking the package would get wet, so I asked him if he could go home during his break.

"Why? Are you there?" John eagerly asked.

I laughed. "No, but I did have a package delivered to you today. I just don't want it to get wet."

"Oh, you mean the chocolates?" he replied flatly. "I got them before I left for work."

John's unappreciative response led me to believe he had expected something else for his birthday.

Now that we were married, I was excited to celebrate John's birthday once again. Even though our marriage had gotten off to a rocky start, I started thinking about how I wanted to surprise him and what to get him. John gave me a hint that he wanted a camcorder. I did some research and realized it would cost me at least $500 to get one. But I wanted to make John happy, so I didn't let the cost change my mind.

The week leading up to his birthday, however, John and I got into a big fight—the biggest we'd ever had. It was about cleaning the shower stall in our bathroom. I told John I would clean it because I would take my time to clean it thoroughly. I didn't mean to imply John didn't know how to clean, but rather that he sometimes rushed. So in this instance, I said I'd prefer to clean the shower myself.

Well, John took it as an insult and decided to prove himself. He squirted cleaning solution in the shower in the morning and let it sit the whole day. Once we got back from dinner that night, I was ready to shower, but the scene in the stall stopped me. The blue cleaning solution had dried out and covered the entire stall.

With some frustration, I went to the kitchen to get the things I would need to scrub the shower. In passing, I let John know what had happened, but his response was a faint acknowledgment.

I tried to scrub the shower, but the solution was so dried out and caked on that I couldn't get it out. Now I was completely frustrated.

"John, I can't get the solution out. Can you try to scrub it, please?" I called out from the bathroom.

"I told you I would clean it," John replied.

"Yeah, but can you do it now? I want to take a shower," I explained while walking to the living room, where John was.

"What's your problem?" John snapped at me. "I told you I would do it. Use the shower upstairs."

"Why should I bring all my things upstairs? I don't understand why you can't just come and clean it now. You're the one who let that stuff dry out in the first place."

I was infuriated. I walked back into the bedroom and slammed the door.

John didn't like that at all. He quickly jumped off the couch, opened the bedroom door, and made sure it would be left open.

"*Never* slam the door again," he said sternly, as if scolding a child.

Who is he talking to? I thought. The sight of John disgusted me at that point.

I walked toward the door to close it again. John walked back to swing it open, and then I closed it again. We shouted back and forth until we were in each other's face. I couldn't recall a time in which I had to defend my strength more than in this moment. I stood straight up, my face raised, staring John down.

"Listen—I'm not afraid of you," I said, looking him straight in the eyes.

He pulled the door open, and I pushed the door closed. John's muscular frame was now towering over me. His body was pressed against mine. I pushed him away from me. His reaction was to push me back.

"You asshole—don't push me!" I screamed.

"You don't push me!" he replied.

The moment had intensified. I realized I was in a situation with someone retaliating with me. I decided to gather my things and head upstairs. As I went up the stairs, I took the time to let John know what I thought about him.

Suddenly, I felt a pull on my arm and I fell. John's hand was now covering my neck tightly.

"Don't you ever talk to me like that! You hear me? DON'T EVER!" John shouted directly in my face as he hovered over me.

I mustered enough strength to pull John's hands away from my neck and push him off me.

"You're sick. You sick asshole!" I shouted back at John, then ran upstairs.

I curled up on the sofa bed in the guest bedroom and cried. I heard the garage door open and close. John left the house.

A few hours later, I heard John return and come up the stairs. He came into the guest bedroom, sat on the chair in front of me, and began to talk with his head held down.

"I've never put my hands on a woman like that before. For that, I'm sorry. I feel really bad about that and what happened. I think it would be best if you went out of town for work this week so we can have time to cool off. I don't think I should be around you right now."

"But I'm not scheduled to go out of town this week," I replied, a bit confused. I wasn't sure how to receive what John was saying.

"Then I guess you can stay upstairs for a while," John concluded, walking out of the guest room and back downstairs.

I spent the next five days upstairs, barely coming downstairs for anything except food. I limited my interaction with John.

It was his birthday that Thursday, and I pondered if I should carry out my birthday plans for him. I decided to still buy the $500 camcorder and a carrying case as well as get balloons to decorate his bedroom.

When John left to work the night shift Wednesday night, I took the opportunity to wrap his gifts, blow up balloons, and put streamers in the bedroom for him to find when he came home in the morning.

The next morning, I heard John come upstairs. He came into the guest bedroom to give me a hug and kiss for the surprise I had left him.

"Thank you for my birthday gift," John quietly said with a smile.

"You're welcome. Do you like it?" I responded with a returned smile.

"I didn't open it yet. I'll wait until later."

"Oh, okay." I didn't have anything else to say.

There was an awkward silence before John finally said, "I'm going to bed. I'll see you later."

We were back in the same bedroom later that night.

In August, John invited his niece and nephews to visit us. It was great spending time with the kids. With John working the night shift during the week, I spent a lot of time with the kids, doing activities and making their meals. John's sisters called me every day to check up on the kids. I had never spoken to his sisters that much since John and I had been together.

When two weeks went by, I asked John what the plan was for the kids, how long they would be staying. John responded as if I shouldn't have asked the question. I didn't see anything wrong with wanting to find out how long the kids would be staying with us. But John received it as if I meant I didn't want them in the house anymore. It was another example of how challenging it was to discuss anything with John without him being defensive about it.

This challenge became more evident a few months later, at Christmas. In December, John and I celebrated our first anniversary at the same place we got married. John surprised me with a beautiful arrangement of edible treats, a card, and dinner. I planned that my gift to him would be me at the end of the night. Even after I explained this, John still commented how he hadn't received a card or anything from me. I guess it was important that he "received" something too.

We decided to invite both our families to Houston for the Christmas holidays. While planning, John and I got into a heated conversation about where our families would stay. John suggested that some family members should stay at a hotel, but I didn't like that idea at all. The whole point was for everyone to be together.

John and I ended up giving up our bedroom to his parents, and my parents had a guest room upstairs. The rest of the family got cozy in the other guest room, while John and I slept on the couches in the living room. Neither of us wanted our parents to stay at a hotel and didn't back down from it. The arrangements seemed to fall into place with everyone staying at the house.

John's family arrived first. His family was larger than mine, as he was the youngest of five children. As soon as John's sister Debbie arrived from New York, the family took off to the grocery store to get enough food for an army. There were bags and boxes of food everywhere in the kitchen. John cleared his family out of the kitchen so we could unpack the groceries.

"Why did you buy so much food?" I asked John.

"What do you mean? We need all this," John replied, confused.

"I mean, we just need food for the next few days. Then we'll go get the groceries for the Christmas dinner we're planning. Right?"

"Um, no. I bought food for Christmas dinner too," John said while reorganizing the freezer to find more space.

"Oh, okay. I didn't know you were going to do that. So, what exactly is on the menu for Christmas?" I asked very sternly.

I wanted to make sure he knew something was wrong. I had been looking forward to John and me coming together to host our families for the holidays. I saw it as an opportunity for us to work on the togetherness in our marriage. But I quickly realized we still weren't on the same page. He didn't even bother to get my input on our Christmas dinner menu.

John looked at me with eyes wide open. He realized he was on the wrong path, but he wouldn't admit it.

"I don't know everything on the menu. We can discuss it tonight," he said, ending the conversation.

After coming home from dance practice for the Christmas concert at church, I went to the bathroom to freshen up before John and I would start preparing the food for Christmas dinner. I came out of the shower, got dressed, then walked into the kitchen only to find John and Debbie already preparing the food without me. I immediately turned and walked out.

Later that night, John asked why I was upset.

"I wanted us to work together to prepare dinner," I responded. "You seem to be doing everything without me. I don't even know the full menu for Christmas dinner. I thought we were going to do this together as a couple."

"That's not true," John started by discounting my feelings. "You were at dance practice, so my sister was just helping to clean and season the meat. We were waiting for you to come and finish preparing it."

"Did I ask you to clean and season the meat?"

John didn't respond but instead went to the bathroom to finish getting ready for bed.

What John saw as his sister being helpful, I saw as being intrusive. He automatically defended his sister and didn't want to see the point I was trying to make.

My parents flew in from Belleville on Christmas Eve to join the rest of the family, and shortly after, John's other sister Veronica flew in from Dallas. I was in the kitchen when Veronica arrived.

"Veronica, you're supposed to take off your shoes," I heard John's mom tell her daughter.

Apparently, Veronica had passed all the shoes gathered at the front door and made her way into the living room with her shoes still on.

"Oh, I'm sorry," Veronica said in an exaggerated way as she walked back to the door to remove her shoes. "When did this start? You guys should put a sign up or something."

Debbie and Veronica later joined my mother and me in the kitchen.

"Here's a cake for John from Ms. Thompson, a close friend of the family." Veronica handed me the cake.

"So, is it for John only?" I cheekily asked.

Veronica became agitated. "Well, yeah. Or I don't know. Ms. Thompson made it for John. I just brought it over."

Debbie had to pull Veronica out of the kitchen to go into the living room.

My mom and I just looked at each other.

I took Mom upstairs to get her settled into the guest room, and I left Dad in the living room talking to John's dad. I came back downstairs to find John and Debbie starting to cook the food for the next day.

"Justyne, do the dishes so we can have clean pots to cook with," John instructed me.

It took every ounce of me to not hit John over the head with something and to tell Debbie to get out of the kitchen. What the hell was going on? So now I was a just dishwasher in my own kitchen?

I ignored John's assignment for me and went upstairs. I was upset that John continued to not involve me in these opportunities for togetherness and even more upset that he sought teamwork with his sister rather than his wife. I was tired of being treated like a visitor in my home and marriage. It was a consistent pattern of John excluding me from his life and doing things that only suited and benefited him.

Later that night, my mother and I went in the kitchen to see what was going on. John and Debbie were in full effect cooking. I was so bothered I couldn't speak. John knew I was upset, but he decided to ignore me and continue what he was doing.

When I stepped out of the kitchen, I overheard Debbie ask John if he was okay. John's response was something I'll never forget.

"Who, *me*?" he said. "*I'm* not bothered at all." His aloof tone was disturbing. It was a complete disregard of his wife.

We somehow managed to get through the rest of the night and the Christmas holiday, but not without a few intense moments and of course no communication.

After the others left, my parents stayed a few days longer. They had a chance to further witness John's disregard of me. They were not happy about it. I made up an excuse for John, saying he was just upset.

"No, no, no," my dad said, visibly upset himself. "That's not right. I don't know any man who behaves the way I've seen him behave. Not one time since I've been here has he given you a hug, held your hand, kissed you—nothing. I see him get into the car, and he doesn't even open the door for you. What kind of man is this?"

My dad is a true gentleman, so he was unfamiliar with John's type of behavior. He wanted his daughter to know she deserved better than what he saw.

I tried to assure my parents I'd be okay and that it was just bad timing to see him at such a stressful time as hosting two families for the holidays.

But even I knew that wasn't true. I needed more time to figure this one out.

11

SECOND YEAR

December 2012 to December 2013

It was three months until John's birthday. We were in our second year of marriage, and I thought it would be good for us to go away for a weekend to celebrate. I did some research and found a great place to eat on Galveston Island Beach plus a hotel to stay nearby. I looked into renting a Jet Ski, seeing as John liked the outdoors.

The day of his birthday, I gave him his gift, a Ninja juicer I had heard him mention from time to time. I told John what to pack for the weekend but kept the details a surprise. Then we put our bags in the car and started the drive to Galveston Island.

The restaurant I found was much nicer than I imagined. It was tucked away in a corner of the beach, with a beautiful view of the sunset over the harbor. Even John had to ask how I had heard about the place.

Moments into our dinner, John mentioned that he had spoken to Blossom, his sister in the Cayman Islands, about coming to Houston to help with the restaurant. I instantly had an unsettling feeling.

"Okay. How long will she be staying?" I asked.

"About three months or so. She'll get settled with us, then eventually get her own car and place to live," John explained.

"So, what will her involvement be in the restaurant?"

"She can help with the kitchen and be the other point person in my absence. And she can also help develop the Caribbean menu so we can have it in place."

As John spoke, I had a disturbing sense about the whole plan. Given how close John was with his family, I worried he and his sister would have more of a partnership than John and I had and were trying to develop.

"I'm not happy about this," I let him know.

"Why?" he asked.

I didn't know how to fully explain what I was feeling. "I just don't think it will be good," I managed to say. "Can you get someone else?"

"Why would I get someone else and not my sister?" John was irritated that I would want to involve someone who wasn't family.

The rest of the evening didn't go well. We didn't talk for the entire meal.

When we got back to the hotel, I tried to explain again how I felt, but it just created more disagreements. John wasn't open to understanding my concerns but rather felt disrespected.

By the next morning, I decided to let it go. I would just wait and see. We concluded our weekend with lunch along the boardwalk, but it was yet another disappointing birthday experience that was becoming way too familiar.

My career was going through some changes as I continued to adjust to my new life in Houston. For two years, I'd been trying to get transferred to my company's Houston office, but to no avail. I was still aligned with my Belleville office, though it was challenging. That office was in a different country with a different currency. And I was still traveling more than I liked.

I decided to cut back on my travel. I wanted to be home so I could adjust to living in Houston as well as build my marriage with John. I fought very hard to secure a local project at work.

However, once I stopped traveling, John got a new job that required him to travel. It was disappointing at first, but then I realized I preferred being home even if he wasn't. After spending the past seven years traveling for work, I could now focus on building stability.

Once my work project ended, I had to look for another in Houston. Unfortunately, there weren't many local projects. Actually, the people who worked out of the Houston office spent most of their time traveling. I started to look for telecommuting projects that wouldn't require travel so I could work from home, but even those were difficult to find.

I came across one project, but it was a junior position. I was too seasoned an employee to be staffed in this role, but I requested it anyway. The project manager said she needed the area director's approval to place me in the role. I let her know I understood. But deep inside, I knew the situation would raise some eyebrows. While waiting for the area director's feedback, I declined projects that required travel, which most people didn't do.

A few days later, I received a phone call from the area director in Belleville. I assumed she was calling to discuss why I'd requested a junior role, how it didn't align with career objectives, and so on. I was prepared to defend my request as a personal reason.

"Hi, Justyne. It's Claudia Smith. How are you doing? How are you settling in Houston?"

"I'm great! Things are going well," I replied.

Claudia didn't mince any words. "So, Justyne, we're moving in a new direction and have decided to let you go. This will give you time to find something in Houston, seeing as you're living there now. Don't worry—we'll give you a great severance package."

My mouth was open. Once I snapped back into the conversation, Claudia exchanged well wishes and let me know that anytime I needed a reference, she'd be happy to help. She then transferred me to HR to discuss next steps.

I was surprised yet not surprised. I had known it was coming, yet I'd never thought it would actually come. I couldn't expect to continue with the Belleville office while living in Houston, especially not if I was turning down travel opportunities. But after the shock wore off, the benefit started to reveal itself. This allowed me to stay home and focus on working with John to open the restaurant.

And that's what I did. For the next six months, I worked on everything for the restaurant—from construction to marketing to operations to human resources and more. I did all I could to ensure John's desire became a reality.

We opened the restaurant in October 2013. We started with a soft opening, then held our grand opening on November 2, the weekend of my birthday. John told me Blossom and other family members were coming up for the grand opening. I asked him to clarify who exactly was coming, but he couldn't say. He wasn't sure if it would be his parents, his two sisters, a family friend, his niece, or whoever.

"How can you not know who's coming?" I asked, incredulous.

"They didn't tell me," he replied with a shrug.

This was a frequent occurrence with his family. They seemed ignorant of the fact that John was no longer single. He was married now. Therefore, they couldn't just show up whenever they wanted and with whomever they wanted without confirming it with both John and me. Whenever I brought this up, John would just get upset and not talk to me, thinking I was callous for even asking.

When we got home from the restaurant that night, I went upstairs to clean in preparation for his family, not sure of exactly who was coming. John apparently assumed I wanted to clean by myself, so he didn't help. Rather, he stayed downstairs talking on the phone with his sister Debbie in New York. When I was done, I went to bed. John stayed in the living room until his family arrived after midnight.

The next morning, I woke up to a full house. I met Blossom, who John now said would be staying for a "few weeks" to help us out. This had changed from the "three months or so" when he first mentioned Blossom. She had a husband and also a young daughter who had just turned three back home in the Cayman Islands.

The weekend was so busy with the grand opening that I forgot my birthday was coming up on Sunday. After a hectic but successful evening, we all came back to the house and went straight to bed. At 12:05 a.m. on November 3, John walked into the bedroom to say happy birthday. He said he hadn't had a chance to get me anything, but he said he would take me out later. I looked forward to what he had in store for us.

In the morning, John got his family to sing happy birthday to me, which was really sweet. I headed to the restaurant while the rest of the family packed to return home, except for Blossom. After the restaurant closed that afternoon, I thought John would take me out for my birthday. But instead, we and Blossom went to the six o'clock church service, then came home. There was no mention of birthday gifts or plans. My birthday already seemed forgotten, even before it officially ended.

Blossom quickly made herself very comfortable. She went straight to the kitchen to cook something John had enjoyed when he was a child. I sat in the living room feeling quite sad and excluded.

John, in contrast, was very happy. He sat on the couch and started to watch Sunday night football. After a while, he turned his head toward me for a moment.

"Are you okay?"

"Yes," I said. I didn't feel comfortable saying anything, seeing as Blossom was in the next room. "I'm going to bed," I concluded.

"So early?"

"Yes," I replied.

"Okay," John said as he grabbed the remote to turn up the volume.

As I made my way to the bedroom, I realized we no longer had our privacy to discuss issues such as these. I decided to send John an email expressing how I felt.

Subject: Hurt

My husband didn't even get me a birthday card or a gift for my birthday. It also seemed liked he didn't have anything planned. Throughout the day, I tried to hold back the tears that were resting in my eyes. It really hurts to know I'm married to a seemingly unloving and inattentive man. It hurts when I think about how I start planning for his birthday weeks before. It hurts when I think about the weeks he has left me by myself to take care of the house and the restaurant, and I haven't complained. It hurts when I think about the time and effort and support I've provided him for his vision and dream to become real . . . yet he couldn't even get me a card. It hurts when I think about the "I love yous" that go unsaid and the compliments about my beauty that are nonexistent. And now I can add a forgettable birthday. Not even a Facebook post.

I guess I'll continue to report to work, keep it business as usual, and think about the husband I wish I had.

Happy birthday,

Justyne.

A few hours later, John came into the room to find me curled up in the bed crying.

"What's wrong?" he asked as he started to wrap his arms around me.

"I sent you an email. You can read it," I replied, trying not to say too much as I continued crying.

"I saw the email, but I didn't read it fully."

I wasn't sure if that were true. Maybe he had read it but said otherwise as a way to encourage me to talk to him. Or maybe he had seen my email but hadn't bothered to read it.

I decided to speak.

"I was looking forward to celebrating my thirty-fifth birthday with you, especially because you know I don't have any friends and family here. You are the only person I have to depend on, and it hurts to know you didn't have anything planned." I barely got the words out. I was still curled up in the pillow as tears gushed from my eyes.

John consoled me and apologized, but not before he defended himself.

"You know how busy it's been. It's not like I wasn't going to do anything for your birthday. I was actually thinking of doing something in the week."

I just listened to John. I struggled to believe what he was saying, seeing as he had never once explained any of this earlier in the day.

The next night, John took me out to dinner at a lovely restaurant. As I looked through the menu, I eagerly let John know I was thinking about ordering the roasted chicken dinner with vegetables and risotto.

"I've got a fifty-dollar budget," he quickly said. "Let's try to stay within it."

I ordered the turkey burger and closed my menu.

The next day, I got a massage at a venue John found online. The place wasn't the greatest. It was a very small office space with old flowered sheets on the massage table and dirt around the bathroom sink and floors. I found out John had purchased the discounted gift voucher the day before. I accepted the gift for what it was and just thanked him for the thought.

Over the next couple of weeks, our new reality started to reveal itself. John traveled to Seattle for work, being home only every other week. Blossom and I were left to spend much time together.

Each morning when I headed into the kitchen, Blossom was there. When I got in the car to drive to the restaurant, Blossom was there, seeing as she didn't drive and couldn't go anywhere unless I drove her. When I worked at the restaurant for at least twelve hours every day, Blossom was there. When I got in the car to drive home, Blossom was there. By the time Monday came around and the restaurant was closed, I locked myself in the bedroom so I wouldn't have to see her.

It became very uncomfortable to share my home and life with someone I didn't know. It was nothing against Blossom. She was a nice lady. But we barely knew each other, and we were very different people. It would have been fine to see her once in a while, but being around her all the time was too much. I'm the kind of person who develops relationships over time, through a gradual process of hanging out and having conversations—not through this intrusive setup my husband constructed and expected me to accept.

One time when John was home, I reminded him about the latest plan, that Blossom would stay only for a few of weeks with us until she found her own place.

"I don't know," he said now with a shrug. "She'll probably be here a couple of months."

This didn't sit well with me at all. The "plan" kept changing, yet he never once discussed anything with me to reach an agreement on this arrangement. I began to resent John. My opinions, thoughts, and feelings were not being considered in this situation with Blossom, yet it impacted me more than John cared to acknowledge. He wasn't even around anymore. We were supposed to be doing this together, but instead we were further apart in every way.

Thanksgiving was approaching, and I decided to head to Belleville to visit my family and friends. I longed for a real sense of home. The house that was supposed to be my home with my husband was far from that.

I told John of my trip. As usual, he had nothing to say. He didn't seem to care that his wife was leaving for Thanksgiving. Perhaps he would have cared if his sister hadn't been there. John and Blossom were very comfortable in their family bond. She had become a crutch for him. He leaned on her instead of confronting and dealing with the issues in his marriage.

I was in Belleville for four days. John never once called me. We spoke only when I called him. In one of our conversations, he let me know his parents and Blossom's daughter would be staying for a few days. They would be at the house when I got home. I received the information as it was told to me.

I dreaded returning to Houston. I knew I was very unhappy in this marriage with John, but I didn't know how to work it through with him. Overall, I thought he had good intentions. But there was such a disconnect between his intentions and how they manifested. He seemed unwilling to see beyond his own perception and unwilling to compromise on a resolution, but I needed him to see things for what they were.

I started to think about Michael a lot. Whenever I wanted to feel loved, I would remember the times Michael and I had shared together. Despite my crazy back-and-forth relationship with Michael, there was love—I mean, *real* love. I felt I could die tomorrow knowing I was loved by Michael, and that comforted me dearly. It made me think marrying John was the biggest mistake. John had the discipline and structure, but Michael had the love and friendship I realized I valued much more.

I headed to the airport and boarded the airplane back to Houston. I found my seat, sat down, and felt compelled to email Michael.

Subject: Hi

It is 4:37 p.m. on December 1, 2013, and I'm on a plane traveling back to Houston from Belleville. The purpose of my email is to let you know I married a good man, but my heart and mind are still with you. After everything that has happened, I'm just amazed how I still think and dream about you. I'm happy when I remember the things we did together. I told my mom that you and I should've been together.

I would like us to talk if you are comfortable with it. Please let me know.

Justyne

When I arrived in Houston, I caught a taxi from the airport. At home, I opened the door and was greeted by John's parents, sister, and niece. I was happy to see them—I really was. I had nothing against them. It was just another reminder that John and I had no privacy to deal with issues in our marriage.

John was away in Seattle for work. I hung out with his family in the living room watching TV before heading to bed. I saw the light on my phone indicating I had a new email. Michael had responded.

Subject: Re: Hi

Justyne,
Your email looks like something I would see in one of my dreams about you. I feel exactly the same way. I recently got engaged to a beautiful woman, and you are still in my heart. Everything seems so foreign without you. I'm not sure why things happened the way they did, but perhaps it was for a reason? I know as well as you do that it would be a bad idea for us to speak on the phone. I'm not sure exactly how to deal with this.
Michael

I read Michael's response at least three time over before I responded.

Subject: Re: Hi

Congratulations—I'm happy for you! I know talking wouldn't be a good idea too. I guess we have to live with the fact that those feelings will not go away. I wish there was a way we could still be in each other's lives and encourage each other in the separate directions our lives have taken. I'll always be here for you. Clearly there is nothing you or I can do that will remove you from my heart.

I guess moving to remote island is out of the question? Joking . . . well, not really. :)
Justyne

I went to bed with a smile on my face and comfort in my heart, knowing I was still loved.

The next day at the restaurant, Michael remained on my mind. There was more I needed to say. I went into the car to get some alone time to write another response to his email.

Subject: Re: Hi

Here is what I really want to say.
I knew that we were supposed to be together. I felt the purpose and the love within our relationship. I wasn't patient with you because I was frustrated by your hesitation and fear. To me, it felt like I was waiting for you to catch up to what I already knew. Things seem foreign to you and me now because we allowed things and ourselves to get in the way of what we really wanted deep inside. I've never been so mad at someone than I was with you from our broken engagement. It truly affected me. I didn't care about anything after that and still know a part of me died after that.

When we last met in Miami, I truly believed I was over you. I felt ready and able to move on, and so I did. Although I still thought about you, it felt like it was where I was supposed to be. But after being married, you were in my heart stronger than ever. What did that mean? I ignored it, but it would come back again and again until I just decided to embrace it. I've thought about so many different things, but one thing I know for sure is that I need my friend in my life. Perhaps our different paths are for a reason. My life is not my own.

I truly am happy for you and wish you all the best. I think I found comfort in knowing that you feel the same way.

Take care,
Justyne

Michael didn't respond.

It was going on two weeks with John's family still at the house. It had been over a month with Blossom. I went to the grocery store by myself, then decided to call John. He was in Seattle and wouldn't be home for a few more days. I thought I deserved to know how long his family would be staying.

The moment I brought up the topic, John's defensiveness started to emerge. The conversation quickly escalated into an argument.

"I don't understand why you can't tell me how long your family will be staying," I said in frustration.

"I will let you know in time," John arrogantly replied.

"Listen—if you can't tell me what's going on, then everyone needs to leave the house. We need some time to straighten things out between us and start over."

Although I was upset, what I said truly had value. But John immediately felt disrespected.

"So, you want to kick my parents out of the house?"

"I didn't say that."

"Yes, you did!"

Our marriage had fallen apart on quicksand, and all I wanted from John was the time, privacy, and space for us to repair it. I didn't understand what hold John's family had on him to cause him to confuse priority with disrespect.

John hung up very upset, and we didn't speak for the rest of the day. When John arrived home later that week, he continued to focus on how he felt I had disrespected his family.

Two days later, I was on my phone checking my emails when I noticed the email thread with Michael was somehow in my sent folder. I opened the email and saw it had been sent to John's email address.

The phone dropped out of my hands.

How did the emails get sent to John? This was unbelievable. I noticed the email had been sent at eight o'clock in the morning, when I was still sleeping. Who could have done this? John's niece, when she was playing with my phone the night before? Had someone else been snooping in my phone?

I had to stop thinking about how it happened and instead focus on how I was going to face John. I felt anxiety all over my body.

When we were at the restaurant that afternoon, I asked John if we could talk privately. From his demeanor, I guessed he had not seen the email yet. We went out to the car. Tears started to swell, and I got very nervous, struggling to get the words out.

John interrupted me. "Did you cheat on me?"

"Not really. I wrote an email to my ex, expressing how I felt about him," I blurted.

John sat still for a moment. "How could you do that?" he finally said. "That is still cheating. You contacted your ex."

"I just sent him an email. Nothing happened. Things are not going well in this marriage at all. I don't even think you love me . . ." I started to explain myself but stopped. "Maybe I should just leave. I don't want to disrupt anything with you and the restaurant with any negative energy. I already feel extremely uncomfortable being here," I said honestly.

John didn't have much to say. "We'll talk about it later," was all he said as he got out of the car and walked back into the restaurant.

I stayed in the car and continued to cry.

I spent the rest of the evening at the restaurant. John and Blossom were in the office, so I sat outside and kept to myself. I felt horrible and wanted to leave. John and I were already not on good terms. Now this had just made it worse.

When we got home, John further expressed his hurt. "I opened my life, friends, family, and home to you. I didn't put a gun to your head when we decided to get married. You choose to marry me. You made that decision. I thought I was marrying for love, but now I don't know."

After listening to John share his feelings, I realized this was about much more than me sending an email to my ex. This was about why I had sent the email in the first place. I tried to get John to think about it from my perspective—the present struggles and unresolved issues in our marriage had shed new light on my past relationship with Michael. I was simply trying to sort out these complicated feelings.

But that didn't go well. John thought I was twisting the situation to be his fault. As he saw it, he was the victim, and there was nothing I could do to make the situation better.

I went to bed thinking about the night Michael and I spent at the Harbourfront, lying on the beach with a picnic basket, watching the sunset. It was a beautiful and peaceful time that always made me smile. I once again remembered what it was like to be loved.

Our second anniversary was coming up. John's parents and niece had finally gone home, but Blossom was staying—and I still didn't know for how long.

John was still hurt, so he didn't want to celebrate our anniversary. When we exchanged text messages that day, John wrote:

> I know it's our anniversary, but I can't be happy. My heart is too heavy.

I tried to encourage John that things would get better and how I'd make changes to better our relationship. I expressed that I would make more efforts in being positive and supporting, seeing as John felt I was only making things more challenging. Although many things were left unsaid and still going on around me, I was still willing to offer something to turn the situation around.

But this wasn't the first time these issues had come up, so John felt he had heard it before. It didn't make him feel better. He needed time to heal.

The following week, I noticed my menstrual cycle was late, so I decided to take a pregnancy test. It was positive.

12

THIRD YEAR

December 2013 to December 2014

On Monday morning, I woke up early and left the house before Blossom saw me so I wouldn't feel compelled to tell her where I was going. I'd made an appointment at the women's clinic to get a certified pregnancy test. The test took about five minutes.

"Congratulations!" the nurse said with a smile. "You're about six weeks pregnant. Your baby is due in August."

I smiled back and thanked her for the confirmation. As I walked out of the doctor's office, I wondered how and when this could have happened. I had hoped John and I would have become pregnant over the last year, but I had given up on trying to get pregnant because John and I couldn't sync our schedules to coordinate the right timing. I had stopped tracking my cycle as well.

Although I was happy that this was finally happening for us, I couldn't ignore the dire state of our relationship. I thought perhaps this was God's way of keeping us together.

I came home and went to the bedroom, thinking about how to tell John the great news. He was out of town for a few weeks, so I wanted to wait until he was back so I could see his reaction in person.

Two weeks later, John returned. Saturday morning, he got up early, as usual, to do his Bible devotions. When I heard him in the kitchen making breakfast alone, I decided it was a good time to tell him the news.

"Good morning!" I said.

"Hey, good morning," he replied.

I stood beside the stove, watching him make scrambled eggs. He looked at me oddly. He had a feeling I wanted to say something.

"What's up?"

"Nothing!" I instantly replied. But then I just decided to say it: "I'm pregnant!"

I excitedly waited to see John's reaction. He held his head down and smiled as he continued to make eggs. Then he turned his face to me.

"Are you sure?"

"Yes. I went to the doctor. I'm eight weeks."

"Wow," John calmly replied. "You know, it's important to eat right and make sure you are thinking good thoughts."

This is where John lost me each time. Whenever I wanted to delight in the happiness of something, he had a way of defusing it with his inability to connect and express emotion. I rolled my eyes. I wouldn't allow his seemingly unattached emotional response rain on the fact that I was pregnant.

"You know," he added with a stern look on his face, "just because you're pregnant, it still doesn't change things." He had to establish that he hadn't forgotten about our issues and how I'd contacted Michael.

That was my cue to leave the kitchen.

We decided not to let the family know, including Blossom, until I was further along in the pregnancy. On a Monday, when the restaurant was closed, I planned to do laundry, only to find that Blossom had done all the household laundry and John's. I kept my own dirty clothes in a separate laundry bag; otherwise, she likely would have done those too.

I was infuriated. She may have thought she was being helpful, but in fact she wasn't. Rather, she was a nuisance. Blossom had a habit of being "helpful" when it wasn't asked for or needed. It made me feel as if I couldn't take care of my own house. I felt undermined. I didn't need her to push herself into my life, not even to do laundry.

Then again, I realized it wasn't entirely her fault. John had invited her into this situation she shouldn't have been in. But what made it worse was that Blossom lacked the common sense and integrity to find her own place and give John and me the space we needed to work things out on our own.

I called John and tried to explain this to him. I wanted him to see that while her doing the laundry was a seemingly helpful thing, it was actually part of the larger problem with this living situation. Specifically, I wanted him to see his own role in it. Apparently, though, my approach was a bad idea.

Minutes later, I heard a knock on the bedroom door. Blossom was very emotional, saying John had just called her. He told her it wasn't her place to do the laundry and that she was "creating problems in the house." I couldn't get a word in edgewise. Each time I tried to say something, she would shout something back. She eventually went upstairs, saying she was too hurt to talk to me. I followed her, but she absolutely refused to talk to me and told me to get out of her bedroom.

I called John back to let him know what happened. "Why did you tell her all those things?" I asked as calmly as I could. "Why did you say she's creating problems in the house? That's not what I said to you and not what I meant."

"You told me you were upset, so I spoke to her about," John said. Wanting to "fix" a problem was a typical reaction for a man.

"Yeah, but you didn't have to say it like *that*," I explained.

"Well, I did what I needed to do," John defensively replied.

It was clear I had put John in a position he wasn't equipped to handle. He wasn't ready to be accountable for his role in what was happening in our home. Instead, he blamed his sister for all the issues.

Over the weeks of my pregnancy, I continued to deal with the growing discomfort of Blossom's unwanted presence and the unresolved issues John repeatedly ignored. I often tried to go along with the situation, but it wouldn't last very long.

Whenever John and Blossom had conversations about the restaurant without my presence or acknowledgment, it upset me. Whenever Blossom was in the kitchen cooking something I had in mind to cook, it upset me. Whenever John and I were driving in the car and Blossom was in the back seat, it upset me. Whenever John and I had an argument and I couldn't say what I wanted to say because I didn't want Blossom to hear me, it upset me.

It was too much. Every day, I woke up with one question on my mind: "When is Blossom leaving?" Many times, I cried out to John, pleading and asking him, "What is the plan? What is going on?" But he'd never give me a straight answer. Each response contradicted the one before. It was obvious he hadn't thought this arrangement out but wouldn't admit it.

John thought that because I was pregnant, Blossom could help me out. But what he didn't understand was that her living with us was an absolute stressor. What I needed was peace and privacy. I needed my home to feel like *my* home. I needed to be able to walk around in my underwear freely. What John thought was help was actually killing our marriage and deeply hurting his wife.

I began to see John and Blossom as one entity I didn't want to be around. I planned a trip to Belleville to visit my family and friends to share my pregnancy news. When Sabrina, my friend from high school, heard the news, she said she'd throw a baby shower for me. My mom took a list of all my favorite foods to prepare for my visit. I looked forward to my trip. It would be a time to relax, let go of the stress, and get the love and support I desperately needed and which my current environment didn't provide.

A few days before my trip, I had my twenty-week ultrasound appointment to get a detailed look of the baby. John was out of town, but he joined by phone on speaker.

The ultrasound went very well; the nurse didn't detect anything wrong with the baby that would cause alarm. John did ask about the baby's heart rate because it had dropped to 148 beats per minute during the procedure. The nurse assured us it was normal and the baby was doing fine.

I didn't want to know the baby's gender, so the nurse told me to close my eyes during that part of the assessment. John already knew what we were having from our twelve-week ultrasound and promised to keep it a secret from me.

Later that night back at home, I started to feel slightly uncomfortable. It wasn't anything serious. I just didn't have much of an appetite. I ate the dinner Blossom prepared, then went to bed.

The next day, I really felt uncomfortable. I called the doctor's office. Because I wasn't bleeding or experiencing any discharge, they felt it wasn't anything serious. The nurse said if I wanted to come in, I could stop in later that day. I planned to go in after my dentist appointment that afternoon. But by the time I was finished at the dentist, the doctor's office was closed.

I went home instead to lie down and take a nap. By the time I needed to pick up Blossom at the restaurant, the discomfort was gone. I felt better the rest of the night.

The following day, the discomfort came back, though I still wasn't bleeding or experiencing any other early-labor symptoms. I thought walking or lying down would make me feel better, which it did.

I came home later that evening to find John home. He surprised me by coming home a day early. I spent the rest of the evening cleaning the bathroom, folding laundry, and packing for my trip to Belleville the next day.

John and I spent time cuddling in bed and feeling the baby move. We tried to get intimate, but John wasn't feeling it. He said my growing belly made him feel uncomfortable, so he rolled off me and went to bed.

I spent the night tossing and turning, trying to find a comfortable position, but nothing worked. I went into the living room to find some comfort on the couch. I don't think John even realized I had left. I turned the TV on, hoping it would put me to sleep. But then I suddenly felt hungry, so I went into the kitchen to get some crackers and orange juice.

The next morning, I didn't feel well at all. The crackers and orange juice hadn't settled well. I threw it up. It wasn't uncommon for me to have stomach pains and vomiting, so I thought it was one of those times.

"Are you sure you can travel?" John asked in concern. My flight was only five hours away. "Maybe you'll have to cancel your trip."

"No. I'll be fine. I just need to lie down awhile," I replied.

There was no way I would miss going home to Belleville. I didn't want to end up staying with John and Blossom. I thought if I could just get home to Belleville, to my family and friends, the baby and I would be okay.

John and Blossom left early to go to the restaurant because John had an interview with a TV station that morning. He made me a cup of tea and put it on the nightstand as I curled up on the bed.

"I'll be okay," I told him. "All I need is a couple of hours to nap. When you get back, you can take me to the airport."

I heard the door close as I reached to take a sip of the tea.

I tried to nap, but the pain intensified. I didn't know what was happening. I kept going to the bathroom, thinking I had to make a bowel movement, but nothing came out. I stripped off my clothes, as I began to feel hot.

I soon began to realize I was having contractions. I was in labor at only twenty weeks.

I called John, barely getting out the words, "I need to go to the hospital!" I lay on the bed, screaming for help, calling out for John to help me.

Suddenly I felt pressure bearing down on my bottom, and I ran to the bathroom. I sat on the toilet and started to push, hoping it was stool.

"*No!*" I cried as I felt my baby exit my body.

I sat there, still, waiting until John got home. I was in complete denial. I heard the doorbell ring. I didn't move. I heard someone knocking on the door. I didn't move. I saw someone walk around the back of the house. It was our neighbor, and she was calling out my name. I didn't move.

"Justyne!" John called out my name as he opened the front door. He walked into the bathroom and saw me sitting on the toilet.

"Oh, sorry!" He thought he was interrupting me, so he started to walk off.

"No! I lost the baby!" I cried out to him.

John's face froze. "No. Oh no," he said.

He came back into the bathroom to pull me off the toilet. I didn't want to move. There was blood everywhere. John grabbed a towel to cover me and walked me to the bed.

"Is it the baby?" I asked him.

John went back into the bathroom. "Yes. It's him."

"It was a *boy*?" I started to cry all over again. It was all becoming real that I had just lost my son.

John and I wrapped our baby in a towel and went to the hospital. He called my mom to let her know what had happened and that I wouldn't be going to Belleville. John also called our pastor so he could pray with us.

It was all too overwhelming. As I sat on the hospital bed, John leaned over the rail with his head down. I saw tears fall from his face. He was crying. He didn't tell me what he was feeling, and he tried to hide his tears, but I grabbed his face to tell him I loved him. He nodded and allowed the tears to roll down.

After two hours, we were able to leave the hospital with a box as a memory of our son. John stayed with me for a while at home before he had to go back to the restaurant. I knew he didn't want to leave me, but I also knew he was needed at the restaurant. I spent the evening on the couch and cried myself to sleep until John and Blossom got home.

John juggled his responsibilities at the restaurant while consoling me. Cherie and her girls came over Friday night to play card games with me. My mom surprised me by coming on Saturday to take care of me for the next few days. John flew back to work on Sunday.

The next few months were the most difficult days I'd ever lived. I had never experienced such loss and pain in all my life. I didn't want to talk to anyone at church, any family or friends. I allowed myself to feel what I was feeling.

Even during that time of mourning, I asked John when Blossom was leaving. Her presence bothered me even more now. I wasn't pregnant anymore, so there was really no reason for her to stay on my behalf.

Of course, John would get upset that I had even asked. I tried to offer suggestions, but he always cut me off midsentence and refused to hear any more. He was very defensive and only received my comments as disrespect toward him and his family. It was a constant back-and-forth battle.

Because I wasn't getting any support from John, I tried to find peace any way I could in the situation. The thought of apologizing to Blossom came to mind. I thought if I explained to Blossom how I felt, it would provide the clarity and peace I was desperately trying to find.

One night at the restaurant, I pulled Blossom aside to sit in the private area of the restaurant.

"I want to apologize for how I've acted toward you," I told her. "It's not my nature to pull away from someone in the way I have with you. It's just that John and I have been married for only a short time. When you moved in, he and I really hadn't had the chance to spend time together. I was uncomfortable with the arrangement because I didn't know you, and I didn't know how long you'd be staying. I'm the type of person who likes to know what's going on."

I cried throughout my whole speech. I genuinely felt bad. I knew the person I had been around Blossom wasn't who I really was.

"Well, thank you for saying this. I receive your apology," Blossom began. "I understand. I can tell you care about my brother a lot. You should try to be more open with him, allow him into your heart. I can tell you are a nice person too. You guys should work together more to get much closer."

With that, the conversation was over.

It wasn't the response or the information I had expected or hoped to receive. I had hoped Blossom would realize how her presence was interfering in the process of John and me building our relationship and marriage. But either it went over her head or she chose to ignore it. I thought having a heart-to-heart with Blossom would change my attitude about her and the situation, but it didn't.

The next day, I woke up with the same question on my mind: "When is Blossom leaving?" This was not going away. I knew at that point the situation with Blossom and the disconnection with John had to change in order for things to get better.

In the midst of the chaos, John and I managed to go to Mexico to attend his friend's wedding. John officiated the ceremony. John and I were still not on good terms, and it was evident throughout the trip. We barely spoke. The silent issues were getting louder.

After the wedding ceremony, I asked John, "How did it feel to officiate the wedding knowing our own situation?" I couldn't help but find it hypocritical.

"No one is perfect," he replied, as if unaware of the polarity of his actions to his own life.

On Fourth of July weekend, John and I had the house to ourselves. Blossom went to New York to visit their sister Debbie. John and I spent time cleaning and doing small fixes around the house, and we even went out together. I spoke more in the car when Blossom wasn't around. I felt free to talk to my husband without someone listening to our conversation.

John decided to invite his friend and her family to the house to join us for the weekend. He might have run this idea by me earlier, but I don't remember if I'd ever agreed. Regardless, I was just happy to get a break from Blossom being around. We and their family drove up to a local lake in Houston to fish with the kids, then we went downtown to watch the fireworks.

We had to leave downtown early, however, to pick up Blossom at the airport. She had called me to say she was on her way home and needed a ride.

My first reaction was, *Home?* Why was she referring to our house as her *home?* Her real home was in the Cayman Islands with her own husband and young child, from whom she had been away for a year by this time.

As soon as she got in the car, my spirit started to fade. I had never wanted to be away from someone like this before. Her presence felt disrespectful. When we all arrived back at the house, I went straight to the bedroom and didn't come back out. John and Blossom continued to entertain the guests.

"Have you spoken to Blossom to find out her plan?" I once again asked John a few days later.

"No, I haven't spoke to her about it."

It had been over a year since Blossom moved in. And every time I asked this question, this was always John's response. It was very hard to believe John hadn't spoken to his own sister about how long she would stay with us and be away from her own family.

I decided to state my thoughts to provide clarity: "We need to start thinking about a long-term plan on how we can function without Blossom—unless she plans on moving here to Houston and getting her own place."

"I'll talk to her about it," John replied.

I had said *we*—John and I—needed to agree on a plan, yet he seemed to think he needed to talk to his sister about it first. It was as if we had to wait for direction from his sister before we could decide what to do in our lives, our marriage, and our home.

Given the growing tension in the house, I started to actively look for jobs that required travel, even though that had never been my plan. When I'd lost my previous job, I was ready to devote my time and energy to building the marriage, enjoying the restaurant, and creating a family with John. I never wanted to travel again; I wanted to build stability and community. But with the brokenness in the marriage, I suddenly I found myself needing to get a piece of my own life back that was familiar. My home was not even my home. It was a place of discomfort and unhappiness I wanted to get away from.

"I'm going to go back to consulting," I firmly told John one night. "I'm going to travel Monday to Thursday so I don't have to be here."

"Okay," he casually replied.

"You do realize the only reason why I'm doing this is because Blossom is here and I don't want to be in the house," I emphasized.

"Well, if you're not happy, then I'm not going to keep you here. I think it would be good if you went back to work and traveling," he said flatly.

I looked at him, completely baffled by his response. On one hand, it was seemingly supportive, agreeing that I should do whatever I wanted to do. But on the other hand, it proved I was dispensable. Whether I continued helping him at the restaurant didn't mean anything to him. Whether I was away for days at a time didn't mean anything to him. I didn't mean anything to him. My heart sank.

John was unwilling to address the issues that were causing our marriage to fail. John was in denial about his sister's unorthodox presence in our home and life. John refused to take a stand to change things to create an environment that was secure for his marriage and wife.

I started to focus on what I needed to do for myself. I applied for several jobs before I heard back from one of the big-five consulting firms. Going through the interview, I was really confident I would get the job. I planned to give John one more chance to realize the issues before I took the job and started traveling.

But that opportunity didn't come. After five separate phone interviews and a trip to New York for the in-person interview, they didn't extend an offer. I was devastated to have gone so far in the process without getting the job.

More importantly, not getting the job meant I would still be stuck in the house every day, and that depressed me. I didn't know if I should just leave now or wait until I found a job. I went back on the computer and applied for more jobs.

Tensions got extensively worse, with long stretches of John and me not talking to each other. One day while he and I drove together to the restaurant without Blossom, I let him have it. It began with him making some remark about me being upset because things were not going my way.

"What exactly has ever gone 'my way'? I moved from Belleville to Houston, where *you* live. I moved into *your* home, not a home we bought together. I sold my car and gave *you* money to finish paying off *your* car. I don't even have a car of my own. I'm working at the restaurant, which is *your* vision, not mine. I'm living with *your* sister. SO WHAT EXACTLY IS GOING MY WAY?" I shouted as I slammed my hand on the dashboard.

In a stupid act of immaturity, John put the windows down—as if he needed others to hear how "horribly" I was treating him.

"I don't care if the windows are down! I *want* people to hear what I have to say!" I continued yelling.

John didn't say anything until we pulled into the restaurant parking lot. "Don't ever talk to me like that. I will not respond if you approach me like that," he directed me, emotionless and cold.

"What does it matter? Regardless of how I speak to you, you don't respond anyway. I'm done with this crap." I looked straight ahead and took a sip of the tea that was still warm in my cup. "Please leave the keys in the car because I'm going to stay here for a while to calm down and finish drinking my tea. Thank you."

About twenty minutes later, I walked into the restaurant and went to the office to start work for the day. Whenever I needed to speak to John, I acted as if nothing had happened. I figured I could start ignoring things too. This surprised John, and he asked to speak to me outside.

"I don't want this to continue, with you arguing with me all the time," he said, seemingly concerned and interested.

I was shocked with how he started the conversation. I looked at him and firmly said, "Listen, we need to address things now. No more excuses. I'm not going to continue doing this mess with you anymore."

"Fine. I'm working on something, and I will talk to you about it tonight," he concluded as if ending a business meeting. We went back inside the restaurant.

It was my turn to be surprised. John was actually working on something. Maybe this meant he finally realized we needed time together, without Blossom, to work things out. Maybe he would tell her to go home for a while until he and I had a chance to get on the same page, and then together we would let her know when she could return and for how long. I looked forward to the conversation we would have later that night.

When we got home from the restaurant, Blossom headed upstairs, and John and I went to our bedroom. I showered and got ready for bed, then waited for John to join me.

"Okay," he started. "I put together a list of things you and I can do to help with this situation. First, we will pray together every night. Second, you will take more interest in cleaning the house. Third, you will apologize to my family . . ."

John continued with his list, each point focusing on me. He schooled me each time I tried to interrupt him. He never came up for air to allow an actual conversation. This was one of his habits. He would often talk without stopping or letting anyone get a word in edgewise. That way, he could go down a path no one else was on.

"Lastly, I've put together a postnuptial agreement for you to sign that will protect both our interests," John concluded.

I sat there in silence. I was so thrown off by John's arrogance, stupidity, and denial that it left me quiet. I didn't have the words to correctly express how I felt. He truly thought that if only I corrected my behavior, things would be okay. He was ignorant to the fact that I was merely responding to the uncomfortable situation he had created for our life.

Finally, I spoke. "You put together a list of things *I* need to do—"

"No, what *we* need to do," John interrupted to correct me.

"Okay, a list of things *we* need to do. Plus you have a postnuptial agreement for me to sign. And that's your solution?" I took a long pause before answering my own question. "I'm not signing anything." As usual, John got upset and went to bed without saying anything else. The conversation was over.

Over the next few days, however, John and I did manage to talk some more. It was a step, even if small. I suggested we go to a marriage counseling retreat for a few days that cost $2,000, but John wasn't even open to hearing more about it. He suggested I move to Seattle, where he was working, so we could be together more often. It was another change I'd have to make to fit John's life. Then again, it would get me out of the house with Blossom and closer to my husband.

"Okay, I'll move to Seattle," I told him one day. "When do you think the move can happen?"

"Maybe the beginning or middle of October," John replied.

It felt great—there was a plan and direction in place.

As the weeks went by and October approached, I often asked John if he had spoken to Blossom about the plan. She would be left in the house by herself, not knowing how to drive.

"No, I haven't talked to her," John would nonchalantly reply.

John's lack of communication was very confusing to me. How could he not discuss the move with his sister to confirm if she would be able to stay and if she was even comfortable with it? I decided not to worry about it anymore. Apparently, I was the only one concerned.

At the end of September, John approached me about signing the postnuptial agreement again. I had hoped by not mentioning it since that first discussion, John would have forgotten about it. But he was still persistent in having me sign.

John said the agreement just stated what was his and what was mine in case our marriage ended. He said we could evaluate it five to ten years from now, if we were still married.

His business approach to this matter made me very upset. I went back and forth with him. I tried to explain I didn't want to sign the agreement because it didn't make any sense. It didn't make the situation better.

"Listen, I'm very serious about this," John firmly said, pushing the papers at me. "We will not move forward unless this is signed."

"Fine!" I scribbled a signature on the unread document and threw it back at John. "Don't put that in my face ever again." I sat on the couch with my head down and hands covering my face. I wanted to cry.

John was taking everything out of me, and I didn't know how to deal with it.

He left later that day to travel back to Seattle for the workweek. The next morning, I received a text from him saying that Blossom was going out of town. That was it—no location or details about how long. A half hour later, I received a text from Blossom asking for a ride to the bus stop. John and Blossom seemed to have coordinated how and what they were going to tell me, which was very little.

Later that afternoon, I dropped Blossom off at the bus station. Even without knowing a thing, I got a celebratory pizza on my way home and cheerfully delighted in it the whole day.

Two weeks went by without a word about Blossom. I didn't ask, and John didn't reveal any information to me. It was now October, when we had planned for me to move to Seattle. John never revealed any more information about that either.

Even without knowing what our plans might be, I took the time to enjoy the house. I bought new carpets and mirrors to decorate the house, making it feel like my own. And with Blossom gone, John and I could work more closely together at the restaurant—mostly because he didn't have a choice with Blossom gone. But it actually worked out for the better. John needed to learn how to build a relationship with me without the crutch of his sister around.

We moved into November with no word about Blossom or my move. My birthday was coming around. I didn't want it to be a repeat of what happened the year before, when I'd ended up crying because John didn't have anything planned and then he quickly put something together with a fifty-dollar budget to pacify me. As I contemplated my plans, I asked John if Blossom happened to be coming back that weekend.

"I don't know," he said, as usual. "I'll have to ask her."

I made my intentions clear. "Well, if she's not coming back, then I'll stay here for the weekend and celebrate with you. But if she is returning, then I'll spend my birthday in Belleville."

John went back and forth to coordinate with Blossom. When he confirmed she was indeed returning that weekend, I let him know I wouldn't be there.

When Blossom returned in November, it was the beginning of the end for John and me. I decided to resume my job search, though I did also look for jobs in Seattle, per our original plan.

John said he supported my job search and that he was praying for me, but I was unsuccessful. With each opportunity, I would reach the last stage of interviewing, but the offer wouldn't be extended. I had never been rejected so much before.

At one point, I started to wonder whether John really were praying that I would get a job and if we were on the same page.

"Hey, what happened with the plan of me moving to Seattle?" I asked him one night.

"Nothing happened. It's still a potential plan," he responded.

"A *potential* plan? You said I could move at the beginning or middle of October. But when that time came, Blossom left. She was gone for the whole month, and you never mentioned the move again. You still haven't mentioned it since she's been back."

"Just because it didn't happen then, it doesn't mean that it won't happen later," John vaguely replied.

"When?" I asked.

"Soon."

I shook my head and went to bed.

For the next few months, John and I exchanged many texts. I couldn't get straight answers by talking to him in person, so I tried sending my questions through text, thinking he would provide a different response.

We need to discuss a long-term plan forward.

John replied:

> The plan long term is that she'll stay at the restaurant whether she lives with us or not.

I tried to explain how wrong he was in his approach, but my efforts were fruitless. He got defensive, turned into the victim, and refused to discuss the issue anymore.

When I reached the third stage of the interviewing process with a new company, I decided not to tell John about the opportunity. The process was going very well, so I wanted to see what would happen if I kept it quiet. All the other job opportunities I had told him about had fallen through. The company was based out of Houston and had limited travel. It was a great opportunity to get back into my career and regain my self-confidence.

In December, our wedding anniversary came and went without John and me celebrating. We spent the day at the restaurant working, like any other day. Soon after, the holiday season approached. I had hoped to hear that Blossom would be leaving to go back home, but it didn't seem as if that would happen. So, I prepared to spend the holidays with my husband and sister-in-law. John's daughter, Josephine, would join us too.

John was planning on being home for a full two weeks after spending a few weeks on the road. I decided to plan a seven-day sex challenge for us to do throughout the holidays. It was a fun way couples could reignite their intimacy by making love every night for a week. I explained to John that it would be a good chance to get closer and try to get pregnant again. Despite the issues we had, I was trying to push through, hoping things would get better. Most of the time, I felt all alone in my attempts, but a part of me believed John wanted to fix the marriage but just didn't know how.

When John's two-week vacation began, he decided to go to Dallas for a couple of days to attend a football game with his friends. John's parents lived in Dallas too.

Okay, I thought. *I guess he can have this time with his friends, so we can have the rest of the time with each other.*

I dropped him off at the car rental agency, as he would leave me the car at home and drive a rental to Dallas. That day, I called him several times during his drive.

"Are you going to see your parents in Dallas as well tonight?" I asked.

"Yes . . ." he replied.

I remember feeling something was off with that response, but I didn't know exactly what.

It was getting close to midnight, and I hadn't heard from John. I called to see if he had reached his parents' house in one piece. With him not calling yet, I was wondering if he was still driving.

"Hey, you're not still on the road, are you?" I asked.

"No," he replied.

"Oh, good. Are your parents awake?"

"I'm not there."

"So, where are you?" I asked, confused.

"I'm in downtown Dallas at Richard's house. I might just stay here for the night."

We talked for a few more minutes until we said good-night. I got off the phone thinking something was off about the conversation, but I didn't think much more of it.

A couple of days had passed, and I anticipated my husband's return. I picked him up at the car rental place.

"So, did you ever get a chance to see your parents?" I followed up.

"No," he said.

We ran a few errands, then went home. As I pulled up in the driveway, John suddenly turned to me and said, "I got a bike."

"Aw, really?" I was disappointed. I had told him the year before that I wanted us to get bikes together sometime.

"Naw, I'm just joking," he said nearly silently.

"Uh . . . okay." With a shake of my head, I got out the car and went inside. I was due back to the restaurant soon. As I was getting ready, John went into the garage, then to the patio. He looked as if he were getting ready to do some gardening. We kissed each other good-bye, and I left. I reminded myself that we could begin our intimacy challenge that night.

Later that night, I drove up to the driveway, opened the garage door, and saw a bike.

Blossom was in the passenger seat. "Ooh, where did that come from?"

I just gave her a look and said, "I don't know." It was one more thing in the house and my life that I did not know.

As I went inside, I carefully pondered how I could bring up the bike without ruining the evening I had planned for John's return. I went into the living room, brought John the mail, and sat down beside him. He was intensely engrossed in the football game on television.

"Hey, hon—I thought you said you didn't get a bike," I quietly said.

"No, I said I didn't *buy* a bike," he responded.

"Huh?"

I was confused. I clearly remembered him saying "got a bike," not "bought." Either way, did John really think there was a difference between *buying* a bike and *getting* a bike?

"So, where did you get the bike from?" I continued to ask.

"Somewhere."

"*Somewhere?* Is it a secret?" I was getting upset.

"No." John kept his response short.

"Where did you get the bike?" I pressed. This was pissing me off. I felt as if I were having a conversation with a five-year-old.

After a long pause, he said, "A coworker."

I was still puzzled as to why he was being private about it.

"I don't understand. Why didn't you show me the bike earlier, when you and I first got back to the house? Why would you be undercover about it?"

"Oh, so you think I'm undercover? Okay. Then, yeah, I'm undercover," John ignorantly replied, completely missing the point. But this was his usual go-to when he felt he needed to defend himself.

"Look, the bike isn't a big deal. But I feel this is the type of thing you hide from me unnecessarily, and I don't understand why. And the way you're responding to all this is making it a bigger issue than it needs to be—"

"Are you done?" John abruptly interrupted. "You are acting so sensitive." He looked back at the television.

I stopped talking, got up from the couch, went into the bedroom, took a shower, and got ready for bed. When I went to the kitchen one last time, Blossom was making something to eat. I said good-night to the both of them.

Later, John came to bed, rolled to his side, and turned off the lights. I guess even a seven-day sex challenge wasn't enough motivation to smooth things over with his wife.

When I woke up, I sensed the tension. I knew John and I wouldn't be talking.

I'd had enough.

If John could be dishonest about the little stuff—the bike, his stops during his trip to Dallas—what else didn't I know? My growing suspicions were becoming too much. There were already far too many incidents when he'd chosen only little details to tell me rather than communicating with me openly and honestly as husband and wife. It didn't make any sense.

I'd had enough.

My constant cries about how his sister's presence hurt our marriage went ignored. Worse yet, he turned the situation around to make me the problem. Blossom living with us was just one of many fundamental decisions that affected both of our lives yet were not spoken about or decided together.

I'd had enough.

John was sitting at the table working on the computer, as he usually did every morning. I sat on the couch beside the table, leaned over, and asked him, "Can you drop me off in Pasadena when you go pick up Josephine?"

"Okay, that's fine," John replied with no questions.

My friend Susan had a home in Pasadena and would be there for the holidays. I wanted to be there instead of here.

John, Blossom, and I got in the car to go to the restaurant. The car was silent with no one saying a word. When we got to the restaurant, I did the things I usually did, then waited in the car until John was ready to leave.

John and I left Blossom at the restaurant and went back to the house. I quickly packed a bag, not knowing when I would return. I took off my engagement ring and wedding band and put them in my jewelry box. I printed the divorce papers I had found online, filled out the information, signed them, then put it all in my bag.

John was in the house for just a couple of minutes to gather some things, then he went back to the car to wait for me. I kept the door open to make sure he knew I was coming and wouldn't drive off. I had my workbag, laptop, and overnight bag in my hands as I got into the car.

John turned to me. "What are you doing with all those bags?"

"I'm going to stay with Susan for a couple of days," I answered.

"Oh, you can stay until next year," John snapped back.

"Okay," I replied.

John drove me to Pasadena to my friend's house. The drive was an hour and a half, and we didn't say a single word to each other. When we pulled up to the gates, John stopped the car long enough for me to get out, then he quickly sped off as soon as the door closed.

Christmas came and went. I didn't call John, nor did he call me. This was not heartbreaking but familiar. I decided to enjoy the holidays with Susan and her family. It was a relaxing, comfortable, and happy time—feelings I hadn't felt for a long time.

After a few days, Susan drove me back to the house. As I approached the door, I didn't know what to expect. I had texted John to let him know I was coming back that day, but he hadn't responded.

I opened the door to see Blossom sitting on the couch watching TV and on the phone. I took off my shoes, said hi, walked past her, and went into the bedroom.

A few hours passed, and I received a call from John's friend Rhonda.

"We are ten minutes away," Rhonda said.

"Okay . . . from where?" I asked.

"From your house." Rhonda paused and waited for some sign of recognition from me. When she didn't get any, she quickly added, "Are you telling me John didn't mention I'm dropping the kids off for the weekend?"

"Nope," I replied.

"I'm going to call John right now and call you back," Rhonda said, then quickly got off the phone. I could tell she was shocked and very apologetic.

John got home a few minutes after Rhonda, her husband, and their kids arrived. He opened the door and greeted everyone else but didn't say anything to me. When I was in the living room, he served our guests some cake in the kitchen, then hid the rest in the refrigerator from me. When he wasn't looking, I made sure I took a piece of that cake.

As the evening wound down, Rhonda and her husband left, and her two boys stayed back to enjoy the weekend with us. After the kids were settled in their room, I got ready for bed too.

As I went to climb into bed, John said, "No." He snatched the covers from my side of the bed. "I don't want to share a bed with you."

"What? Don't be crazy," I replied, placing my pillow on the bed.

"No, I'm serious. You can sleep on the couch." John threw my pillows on the floor and spread himself across the king-size bed so there was no room for me.

I was disgusted. He would rather put his wife out on the couch than deal with the issues. It was as if he wanted to teach me a lesson, to punish me.

That was the end for me. I pulled out the divorce papers, and I told John to sign them.

"If this is the way it's going to be, then I don't want this or you in my life," I said. "Here are the divorce papers. Just sign them so we can get on with our lives."

I felt the heat in my face rising. I truly did not like the person I'd married. In that moment, I knew John was not the person I wanted to spend my life with nor even another minute with.

John threw the papers back at me. I went out to the couch.

Days passed with the divorce papers looming between us. New Year's Eve was approaching. One night while on I was the couch, John asked, "Where are the divorce papers you want me to sign?"

"I still have them," I replied. "Do you want them now?"

"You can give them to me tomorrow," he said, then he walked into the bedroom and closed the door behind him. Shortly after, I made plans with Susan and some other girlfriends to spend New Year's in Pasadena.

I left the restaurant early on New Year's Eve to return to the house and pack. I opened the door to see John sitting at the table on the computer.

"You're here early," he said, surprised to see me.

"Yes. I'm going to Pasadena with Susan and some other girls for New Year's Eve."

"Really." He sounded upset. "When were you going to tell me?"

"Now," I replied.

I walked into the bedroom to pack my things, going from the bedroom to the kitchen to make sure I had everything I needed for the weekend.

"Where are the divorce papers I told you to give me?" John said, trying to regain control of the situation.

I retrieved the papers from my bag, gave them to him, and continued packing.

"So, what are your plans? Where do you plan to go?" he asked while reviewing the papers.

"I don't know yet. I'll see."

I truly didn't know what I would do, but I knew I would do anything to get out of this foolish mess.

"Do you plan to stay in the United States? Remember—you just have your permit," John reminded me.

I shrugged. "I don't know if I'll leave the country."

"Well, I'll just have to call immigration to let them know," John informed me.

I shook my head as I cracked a smile and listened to him.

As I got my bags and headed out the door to wait for the taxi to take me to the bus station, John picked up the phone and called someone. It seemed he wanted to tell the person what was happening, but he hung up before saying a word. How can you tell someone, "I let my wife go"?

I met up with Susan, Allison, and Tracey at the bus station in Pasadena. I was ready to have an amazing New Year's. To smile, laugh, and celebrate what I believed would be an amazing year ahead.

Susan found a church for us to attend. As you get older, the lure of New Year's parties wears off, so you either go out on a date or you go to church. Church it was! We got there just in time before the music started.

I couldn't stop smiling. I was happy to be where I was. I felt present. As I got into the praise and worship of the music, memories of the past year flashed in my mind. I knew I wasn't in a good marriage. I knew I wasn't married to my best friend—much less any kind of friend. I knew I wasn't myself. Something had to change. And since I could not even have a conversation with my husband, I knew God had to make that change.

The pastor started his sermon. It was uplifting and relevant. At the end of the sermon, he labeled the new year as "Fabulous '15." Yes! That stuck with me. I believed it would be a fabulous 2015. I declared it.

Once I claimed it, these words resonated into my spirit: *You'll go back a little, but you'll make a huge leap forward.*

I thought perhaps it meant my marriage would take a step back in order to take a huge leap forward. Or maybe it meant I would eventually make a huge professional leap forward. It really could have been anything, so I held on to it so it could guide me into and through the new year. Several months later, I would understand what it truly meant.

After service, we went back to Susan's family home to eat, chill, and laugh. It was such an awesome time. It reminded me of the normal I once knew and wanted back.

The next evening, I received a call from John.

"I need to know when you're coming back here so I know how to plan things," he said.

"I was planning on coming back on Monday."

I knew John was flying out on Sunday, and I had intentionally booked my return bus trip for Monday.

"Well, the bedroom door will be locked, and I will leave your things outside in the living room."

"You can't do that—I have my things in the room!" I was in complete shock.

"You left here without letting me know where you were going, so your stuff will be outside for you," he said sternly without pause, as if he truly believed this logic justified his actions.

I had told John I was going to Pasadena with Susan—the same place where he had dropped me off before Christmas. Yet he'd convinced himself that I'd left the house without letting him know where I was going or with whom I would be.

"Fine, I'll be back before you leave on Sunday."

I didn't want to argue with him any longer—it wasn't worth it. I changed my ticket and was back at the house the following day.

When I got to the house, no one was there. I headed toward the bedroom, and the door was in fact locked. I sat on the couch and waited for John and Blossom to get home.

After a couple of hours, I heard the garage door open. It was them. No words were uttered to me. John opened the bedroom door. I went inside and stayed there until he was ready to leave for his flight. Blossom had packed John's bag with food. She kissed his forehead as she handed it to him, then she headed upstairs to her room.

Before John walked out the door, he reminded me that he still didn't think I should be sleeping in the bed.

PART III
A NEW BEGINNING

13

THE MONTH AFTER I LEFT

March 2015

It had been a tumultuous February—leaving John, facing the restraining order, and losing my job. After I gave Cherie the items John had requested, I didn't hear from him for a while.

I was so grateful to Michelle and Doug for opening their home to me and helping me navigate the separation with John. I spent the next month and a half with them as they counseled me. It was the best thing that had happened to me since I'd moved to Houston. I instantly felt myself get back into *myself* after years of being depleted in a bad situation.

I focused my time on getting a new job as soon as possible, seeing as the last one had fallen through in such an unfortunate way. One of the companies I had applied to in Seattle contacted me for an interview. Although I no longer planned to move to Seattle to join John anytime soon, I still decided to interview with the company, given they were named as one of the best consulting firms to work for. I had a few other interviews with companies in Houston and even some interviews with companies located in other cities.

I found it interesting that once I stopped telling John about my job opportunities, I started getting offers. A couple of jobs required traveling, but I turned those down because I knew that truly wasn't my heart's desire. I continued to pursue local opportunities and still kept Seattle in mind.

It eventually came down to two positions I had to strongly consider: one with the consulting firm in Seattle and another with a consulting firm headquartered in Indianapolis, but I could work remotely from Houston. The executives from the Seattle firm put together an attractive offer that considered my moving costs.

The idea of moving to Seattle was frightening. I never would have thought of moving there had it not been for John working there and our plan to be together. But now things were different. If I moved there, I wouldn't be with him. Yet I had to really consider this great opportunity to reestablish my career and have a new beginning.

I called the HR recruiter in Seattle to have a one-on-one conversation about the opportunity. I had a lot of questions. It turned out to be a very helpful conversation.

"I hope I've provided a bit more information about the position to help your decision," the recruiter said as we wrapped up.

"Yes, you have. Thank you. I just want to be sure that moving to Seattle will be the best decision right now. How is the weather there?" I asked to extend the conversation.

"It's really nice here. We're just coming out of winter, and it wasn't too bad this year. Spring and summer here are so beautiful. I think you would like it."

"That sounds good," I replied as I continued to ponder the decision in my mind. "Actually, I think everything you've said sounds good. I've really enjoyed everyone I've spoken to during the interview process, and the offer looks good."

"Great! So, are you accepting the position?"

"Yes. Yes, I am." The words slowly came out of my mouth as I consciously heard what I was saying.

"Wonderful! I'm really excited. I know this will be a great opportunity for you. The team will be so excited to have you join us." I heard the sincerity in her voice, and it calmed my fears and hesitation.

After the conversation, I felt more comfortable and immediately started planning how I would move, where I would live, and when I would leave Houston.

Michelle and Doug headed out for their spring break family trip, and they were kind enough to allow me to house-sit. This provided me time to look for places in Seattle, start packing, and look for a car. After calculating the costs of a truck rental for the move, it made more sense to just buy a car and drive up to Seattle with a trailer. I would need to buy a car when I got there, anyway.

I called Ken, who worked for a car company, and he connected me to a sales agent who talked me through the process of buying or leasing a car. Ken and Kathy had come to the house that night I'd left John, and Ken always checked up on me to ensure I was doing okay.

After getting off the phone with the sales agent, I couldn't help but ask myself, *What the heck am I doing?* I had no money. I had nothing more than a job offer letter. My mind went in circles asking the same questions. Then I heard a quiet voice in my spirit say, *It's okay . . . It will be okay.* The next day, I signed a lease for a brand-new car.

A few days later, I received an email from John asking to meet up so we could sign the divorce papers. I let him know I had ripped up the divorce papers I had originally given him. John's friend Peter and even Michelle and Doug had all convinced me to hold back on the divorce to allow time for us to fight for our marriage. I was hesitant about meeting John, but he insisted. I decided to do the right thing and meet him.

It was a Saturday afternoon, and John said to meet him at the library at two o'clock. I arrived before he did, sat at a table for four, and waited. When John arrived, he was on the phone wrapping up a call. He walked toward the table while putting the phone in his pocket. He sat across from me on the opposite side.

"Well . . ." John started.

"Hi," I responded.

"Where are the divorce papers?"

"I told you, I don't have them."

"Okay, so what are you going to do?" John hastily asked.

"If you want a divorce, then you'll need to fill out the papers," I nervously responded.

"Oh, really. And we need to settle some money issues too." He started listing the things he thought I needed to give him.

"If you want to talk money, then we'll need to go through all the things I put into the house and divide it from there," I explained.

"That's what the postnuptial agreement was for," he boastfully replied with a smirk.

I looked at him and shook my head.

The conversation didn't last much longer. I mentioned the loan that had to be repaid, and he told me he was going to deduct the money I owed him from the payments.

"You can't do that. That's illegal," I calmly said.

But John couldn't control his temper. He got up from the table and stormed out of the library. I stayed seated and watched him leave.

John had issues he didn't even realize.

As I drove back to Michelle and Doug's home, John called me to say I owed him the remaining balance of what I'd taken from the savings account as well as $1,900 for taxes he filed.

"John, that doesn't make any sense. I'm not even working, so how could you claim me as a dependent on your taxes and I owe you money? What would have happened if you didn't claim me as a dependent?"

"Well, you'll need to talk to the accountant about that, but this money needs to be paid."

"That doesn't make any sense," I repeated. "I think we need to go to a counselor to talk about this."

"Before that can happen, you need to apologize for everything you have ever done to me!" John concluded before hanging up.

Later that night, I received an email from John that started a thread over the next few days:

Subject: Following up

Justyne,
You gave me the divorce papers over Christmas. I signed and returned them in early January. Please tell me why you refuse to give me the final copy to sign.
Thanks,
John

Subject: Re: Following up

John,
After you signed and returned those papers, I received a text from you to rip up the papers (on Peter's behalf). Whether the papers were discarded then or a few weeks after, we would still be where we are today.

During this time of separation, God has truly blessed me in opening my heart to go through this process with you in the correct and godly way. I don't believe God would want us to end the marriage this way. I do believe we started this marriage with two inherently different views and frameworks on how marriage should work, which unfortunately left us both frustrated, angry, and attacking each other for what we needed from each other. It would be great at some point to be able to get on a neutral page with you so that we can go through this in a healthy way in which we both grow and come to a better understanding of the situation.

I have never meant to intentionally disrespect you, cause you hurt, or make you feel unappreciated during our marriage. If you feel I have, for that I am deeply sorry.

I'm committed to turning this over to God and allowing what is to happen, happen. I know you said in February when we spoke that you have come to a decision you are at peace with, so if you feel that is in your best interest, then that is your decision. But I don't believe God would want us to end the marriage in this way.

Good night,

Justyne

Subject: Re: Following up

Justyne,

Peter wanted you to destroy the papers—not me. I merely relayed Peter's message.

Again, you gave me the divorce papers in December. Now you're spinning it on me. Why can't you admit giving them to me and be accountable for what you started?

John

Subject: Re: Following up

John,

In my earlier response, I did not deny giving you divorce papers. This is not about spinning it on you now.

I have let you know, very clearly, where I stand, what I believe, and how I think we should

go through this process. I no longer have divorce papers because I believe we should take divorce off the table to go through this process in a godly way.
Justyne

Subject: Re: Following up

Justyne,
I too have been very clear about where I stand.

You left during Christmas and New Year's without a word. You didn't tell me you were leaving or where you were going or who you were with. I didn't know how to reach you or when you would be back.

Since we first got married, you have threatened divorce many times. You even gave me divorce papers and filled them out, saying all I had to do was sign to make it "easy" for me. You demanded that I sign them that instant, but I refused. But after you kept asking me about the papers, and after I gave it a lot of thought, I signed and returned them to you. You were glad to take them with the slightest hesitation.

Over these last three years, you have left me with SUCH pain and sorrow—too much. So, will you now sign the papers? Let's be civil, just as you said when you started this whole thing. Let me know ASAP.
Thanks,
John

Subject: Re: Following up

John,

You don't seem to be ready to face the truth about yourself in this situation, and that is truly unfortunate. I have no intentions of going through this with you in an uncivilized manner.

Thank you,

Justyne

John didn't respond.

It was now the last week in March, and I had most of my things packed and ready for my move. I bought a plane ticket for Sabrina, my high school friend, to fly from Belleville to Texas to help me drive to Seattle. The next day, though, Sabrina realized she was scheduled to work the weekend when I needed her help. She suggested her boyfriend, Steve, could help me instead. I was nervous to drive over thirty-five hours with another man, but I guessed it was better to have a man's protection in this situation.

I requested that my start date be March 30, which meant I could still attend Cherie's wedding before the move. Yes, Cherie had met the man of her dreams, and I wanted to be there to celebrate with her, especially after all the support she'd provided me. I planned to leave the morning after Cherie's wedding.

It was Saturday, moving day! I said my good-byes to Michelle, Doug, and the rest of their family. I hitched a rental trailer to the back of my new car, and everything I had and acquired was packed in it. I asked Michelle, Doug, and other church members to not tell John I was leaving or where I was going. After everything John did to try to destroy me, I didn't want him to know what I was doing in my life and that I would be in Seattle, where he traveled regularly for work.

I headed off to the airport to pick up Steve. I was thankful to have Sabrina and Steve as dear friends in my life. Whenever I needed help and support, they were always there. And now, for the biggest transition in my life, they were the only people from Belleville I would rely on to help me through this.

Steve and I quickly got something to eat, then immediately started our thirty-five-hour drive to Seattle. About five hours into the drive, I received an email from John.

Subject: Moving On Cont'd

Justyne,
I filled out the divorce papers, just as you did in December. Come to the courthouse at 3:00 p.m. so we can sign and turn them in.
John

I didn't want to let John know what I was doing or where I was, so I provided a quick response.

Subject: Re: Moving On Cont'd

Hi, John—
I'm not able to meet you tomorrow. I'll let you know when will be a good time.
Thanks,
Justyne

John didn't like that very much and responded within minutes.

Subject: Re: Moving On Cont'd

You not being "able" to meet tomorrow tells me nothing. It's not like I'm forcing you or something.

You're the one who started all this, right? Let's finish it. I need an exact time when we can do this. I won't sit here, hanging around, waiting for you to be "available."
John

I found it funny that John wanted definitive answers, seeing as he never seemed a fan of providing them to me during our marriage. I didn't respond but rather decided to speak to a lawyer before I replied.

Sunday at six o'clock in the evening, Steve and I pulled up to my new apartment in Seattle. The city was softly lit, as the evening was winding down. The trees that filled the city were beautiful and breathtaking. I felt I had entered a new world. I took a deep breath and exhaled the fresh air. Steve was tremendously helpful as we unloaded my things. He stayed an extra day to return the trailer, pick up a couch, and set up my new TV.

After I had settled in Seattle and started my new job, I sent John a response to his earlier email. I'd had a chance to speak to an attorney to get some advice on what information I needed if John was persistent about going through with a divorce.

Subject; Re: Moving On Cont'd

Hi, John—
I hope this email finds you well!

I know you want to proceed with the divorce process quickly, but we will not be able to proceed with the signing of the divorce papers until a few things are resolved and clearly understood.

I've received letters from the IRS confirming receipt of documentation that has been filed on my behalf for the restaurant. I will need to clearly understand how I am structured in the restaurant.

Can you please provide a copy of the corporation documents/records for the restaurant and the tax filing documents/statements for the past two years, in which I was included? Since I wasn't aware that you would be filing taxes on my behalf, it is important that I have knowledge of what has been filed for my own tax purposes.

The business loan is up for renewal in July this year. Can you renew this loan on your end before this time? If not, we will need to put in place an agreement that states I will continue to have full involvement in the restaurant and that it cannot be sold, transferred, etc. without my involvement and signature—until the loan is paid off. This agreement will need to be notarized and legally enforced.

I would like to avoid any legal stuff as much as possible, but it is dependent upon the settlement of the loan.

If you would like to talk about this more, let me know.

Take care,

Justyne

John didn't reply. A month later, I emailed John to follow up on the email, but again I got no response.

The following month, it was John's birthday. I decided to send him a short email to acknowledge his birthday. John didn't reply to that either. It seemed he was no longer responding to anything I sent him.

The day after his birthday, I decided to visit John at the house where he was staying in Seattle. I thought it was time to let him know that I was also in the city and that I was available to talk whenever he was ready. But he didn't even answer the door.

I spent the next few months enjoying living in a new city. I didn't know anyone when I moved to Seattle. It was a brave and bold move, but one I knew I had to make. I was now enjoying my life in such a brand-new way. I was working in a new job that gave me more satisfaction than I could have ever imagined. It didn't feel like a job; it felt more like an extension of my life. Every day, I met new people who introduced me to things to do in the city. They didn't know how grateful I was and how much I needed it.

I went home alone to a space with only a TV, a couch, and an air bed. I was living a minimalist life—and I loved it. In spite of what I was going through, I was happy. There were random moments when I would laugh out loud because of how happy I was.

My happiness didn't come from the fact that I was separated from my husband. Rather, it came from how much clearer life was to me. Who I was came back to me; I regrounded back to myself.

John and I were on the wrong path, going in the wrong direction. And regardless of what I said, I wasn't able to get him to see that. Something had to happen—something drastic had to happen for John and me to wake up, realize the situation, and decide how and whether we would move forward. I saw this moment as an opportunity for John and me to make ourselves and our marriage better. To make our marriage great. However, I couldn't be the only one who saw it that way.

I tried to contact John again by email, but he remained unresponsive.

The day John didn't open the door, I believed I would never feel positive about the situation again. But after a while, I started to forgive John and understand what was happening. It was a frustrating time, yes. But I realized the only thing I could do was to remain still and openhearted to allow God to work through the situation and to be ready for when the answer would be revealed. I continued to enjoy concerts in the city, eat at new restaurants, meet new people, and excel at my new job. I was truly in a place of peace.

Several months had passed as I awaited to hear from John, but there was still no communication. In a final attempt, I decided to send John one last email in July.

Subject: Clarity and Direction

Hi, John—

I hope you are doing well. I've been praying—asking God for clarity and direction on our situation and essentially to help order my steps in how we move toward restoration.

In the past several months, you've been unresponsive to emails, phone calls, and text messages. I understand that I may have caught you off guard by showing up at your house when you may have not been ready to talk yet. It was my way of trying to open some kind of communication between us. But I'm sorry that it was misconstrued as anything else. Regardless of how this situation ends, there should be some communication in order for us to deal with this in a civil manner.

I'm still willing to go to a counselor with you to help guide us in some sort of direction. I'm available to attend counseling with you while you are in Seattle. You can choose a counselor, or we can ask someone to recommend one for us.

I would prefer that we both surrender to God and resolve what is needed among each other.

I hope to hear from you soon.

Take care,

Justyne

I sent the email to John, then printed and posted it by certified mail to ensure he received it. I also sent the email to the pastor's wife and a deacon he was close friends with back in Houston, in hopes they would be able to talk to him. I wanted to be sure I tried everything before I made a decision that would impact my life forever.

14

THE DECISION

July 2015

I was at work when I received the phone call.

"Hi, Justyne. It's Deacon Patrick. I want to talk to you because I had a conversation with John. Is this a good time?"

"Yes, it is." I walked into the hallway to talk in private. "How did it go?" I eagerly asked.

"Well, John doesn't seem ready to reconcile. He seems to have a hardened heart. He said some stuff, but none of it made sense. I directly asked him, 'Do you plan to reconcile with your wife?' He responded, 'Not at this time.' I'm really surprised and disappointed at his immaturity. He made comments about you being manipulative. I would suggest that you do what you need to do to protect yourself, because I don't see a reconciliation happening anytime soon," Deacon Patrick firmly said.

"I just don't understand why he doesn't want to talk about this," I replied.

I was a bit surprised but not completely. I hadn't heard from John in several months, so I wasn't expecting a full-circle moment. But I thought he'd at least give some definitive thoughts on how he felt and what he wanted. I tried to still give John the benefit of the doubt—maybe he just needed time to get through his feelings.

"I don't understand either, Justyne. He sounds angry and not ready to deal with this in the right way. I don't know if he'll ever be ready," Deacon Patrick said.

"Okay. Thanks for your help and support in this. I'll have to decide my next steps."

"You're most welcome, Justyne. You take care of yourself, and I'll speak to you soon." Deacon Patrick hung up the phone.

I was perplexed, feeling I was forced to make a decision that John and I should be making together. I went back into the office, sat at my desk, opened my laptop, and continued to work.

I went home that night questioning what I had been praying for all this time John and I had been separated. I truly prayed for God to change my heart toward the marriage to make reconciliation possible and to make it clear what I needed to do. I was happy knowing that my heart was completely released from any anger, regret, and unforgiveness. I felt free, yet I was still in limbo, not knowing what direction my life was heading. I was waiting to hear from John so we could make the decision together with clear minds and hearts.

A few days later, I received an email from Deacon Patrick.

Subject: FYI

Hi, Justyne, this is the message I sent to John, with his response.

[Me] Hello. What is the best way for your wife to speak w/ you? She would like to speak w/ you.

[John] I will touch base with Justyne if she provides her current contact information. Or she can call 914-555-4563.

I read the email twice, maybe even three times, in shock of John's arrogance. First, he didn't recognize me as his wife. And second, the number he provided looked like his sister Debbie's phone number in

New York. This infuriated me. I calmed down and replied to Deacon Patrick's email.

Re: Subject: FYI

Thanks, Deacon Patrick.
I've called and texted John from my current number, so he has always had it.

It wouldn't be wise to provide John my address without knowing his intentions, especially since he has not expressed any interest in my whereabouts or well-being . . . ever.

Why did John provide a New York number for me to call? It looks like the number for his sister who lives in New York.

If John has true intentions of touching base with me, he absolutely can, because my number and email address have not changed.

I'll wait until John decides to respond to my many emails, text messages, or calls.
Thanks again,
Justyne

I was devastated. I started to look online for divorce mediators to start the process. I contacted many places. I had never been through something like this before. I hoped it would be a smooth process, seeing as it was clear John didn't want to repair the marriage and I couldn't repair it on my own. I thought perhaps it could be an uncontested divorce process, in which we both agreed on the marital settlement. There weren't many assets between us to distribute, except for the outstanding loan for the restaurant. John had continued paying monthly for the loan, so I didn't think it would be a problem.

I spoke to Brenda from Texas Friendly Divorce. She offered to email John at no charge to outline the services and next steps.

Although John had been unresponsive to me, maybe he would respond to Brenda's email.

While speaking to my girlfriend Allison back home in Belleville, I told her about my challenges in getting John to respond to my emails and how he was telling people he didn't receive them. She mentioned a software application to track emails to see if the person opened it. *Really!* I was intrigued. I installed it on my computer and used it from that day on, every time I sent John an email. I wished I had known about it before.

After Brenda sent John the email to discuss the service and next steps, I sent a follow-up email and tracked it.

Subject: Texas Friendly Divorce

John,

In order for us to have a simplified divorce, there needs to be a marriage settlement agreement.

The only thing outstanding is the loan. I would need to know if you are going to renew it on your side.

If you don't renew the loan, and it remains outstanding, then the divorce is contested, and we go to court.

How would like to proceed with this—do you plan to contest the divorce?

I've reached out to Brenda from Texas Friendly Divorce to mediate this process and file all the necessary paperwork on our behalf.

Thanks,

Justyne

The next morning, against my better judgment, I decided to call the number John had provided in his response to Deacon Patrick. I had a good feeling I would get Debbie, but I called anyway with hopes of reinforcing the need for John to respond to me.

The phone went to voice mail.

I called again.

"Hello," Debbie answered this time.

"Hi, Debbie. It's Justyne."

I paused to hear the reaction.

"Hmm," Debbie replied in a bothered tone.

Debbie and I had never developed a good relationship. And with John and me separated, I could only imagine what he was telling her about me.

"John provided your number to call to reach out to him," I started. "I'm not sure why, but I've been trying to contact him, and he has been unresponsive."

"Well, I told John I can take calls for him. He's dealing with a lot and has a lot on his plate right now. I'm sure he has reason to not respond to you," Debbie snarled.

I remained silent, trying not to react to Debbie's rude remark. She had some nerve to say John had a reason not to respond to me. What did she know, aside from what her little brother wanted to tell her?

"Anyway, tell John I want a divorce, and he needs to respond to the emails I've been sending him."

"You want a *divorce*? Ugh!" Debbie said smugly. "Well, if you want to do that, I'm sure you can go ahead and do that on your own. And I don't believe you've actually tried to contact him. Have you called him?"

I hesitated. I truly didn't want to engage in a conversation with her. Still, I couldn't help but reply. "Yes, I have," I responded.

"I don't believe that."

Who the hell cares what you believe? Why was I even on the phone with her when I should have been speaking with my husband? It started to disturb me. She was ignorant to everything that had happened, yet she was speaking as if she had a voice in the situation. I had to do my best to not respond to Debbie's remarks. My intention was just to give her brother a message, not get in an argument with her.

"Well, whatever. John needs to respond to the email I sent so we can file the right paperwork," I said, bringing the conversation back to focus.

"Okay, I'll let him know. But he has a lot on his plate right now, so I don't know if he'll respond. Is that why you've been talking to other people?"

"Debbie, John has been unresponsive. I contacted Brenda from Texas Friendly Divorce, and she sent an email to John to begin the mediation process."

"Don't say my name!" Debbie venomously said. "I'll let John know."

"Okay," I responded, hoping to end the conversation.

But Debbie had to get the last word in by adding an assumptive remark. "And I would appreciate if you would stop talking to people—"

"JUST TELL JOHN TO RESPOND. HE HAS BEEN UNRESPONSIVE. THANK YOU. HAVE A NICE DAY!" I shouted at Debbie to drown out the ignorance coming out of her mouth.

I eventually heard the phone hang up, and I hung up too.

I was annoyed. Really annoyed. To begin with, what the hell did she know? John had apparently painted a picture that I was talking to anyone and everyone about him, which was far from the truth. Only a few people knew what was going on—Cherie, Ken and Kathy, Doug and Michelle, and Deacon Patrick. These were John's close friends and trusted people from the church who were trying to provide godly counsel to the situation. Many of them had seen John's true colors for themselves. I didn't have to say anything. So what Debbie thought was being said, was perhaps those close to John putting a mirror in front of him.

It was disturbing how unresponsive John was about the situation—yet he was in complete denial about it. And it was even more disturbing to know how his siblings enabled his childish behavior.

Over the next few days, I retained a lawyer to officially start the divorce process.

15

THE TRANSITION

August 2015

Despite everything that was happening, being in Seattle was a breath of fresh air. The darkness that had surrounded my mind and spirit was completely lifted. That's not to say my husband was darkness; rather, the environment in which we were living was darkness. So much went unsaid, ignored, and tolerated.

I was happy because I was in a place of peace and clarity. I knew what was going on around me. I had a voice, and it was stronger. I could hear myself, and it sounded amazing. I heard the voice of the woman I used to know. Vibrant, excited, and passionate about life. My feet were firmly planted back on solid ground and this time not easily moved.

Since separating from John, many things about who he really was had come to light. The secrets he held tightly slowly began to reveal themselves, and his weaknesses were now all he displayed. Usually separation allows couples time to calm down emotions so they can address problems. But John saw it differently.

I attended a wine tasting in the city just weeks after moving to Seattle. I found a Meetup group online that caught my interest, so I decided to check it out.

When I arrived at the event, I saw a woman sitting at the entrance who seemed to be waiting for someone. "Hi, are you Joyelle, the organizer?" I asked.

"No, but yes. I mean, I'm not Joyelle, but I'm one of the organizers!" The woman laughed at her initial response. "My name is Heather. What's your name?"

"I'm Justyne," I replied with a smile.

"Great! We're just waiting for a few more folks before we go inside," Heather replied.

She had such a cool ease that made me feel comfortable. I was glad I'd decided to come out.

Five more ladies joined us for the event. I was glad they were all in my age group. Essentially starting a new life when you're over thirty-five isn't an easy thing. I had found myself in a new city once again. From Belleville to Houston, and now Seattle. I had left my hometown to move to Houston to marry a man I thought would be my forever. But three years later, I was in Seattle, rebuilding my life from what seemed to be years of hurt, pain, disappointment, and loss.

"So how long have you been in Seattle?" asked Tiffany, one of the women who joined us.

"Um, for about two weeks," I said with a smile.

"Wow! That's awesome—you've already got yourself plugged in," Tiffany replied, seemingly impressed.

"Yeah, that's really good," Heather chimed in. "I remember when I moved here, I started meeting people in my first week. A lot of people are transplants to Seattle, so most people can understand how it feels to move to a new city."

Wow, I wished I had this kind of support when I first moved to Texas. I was happy to be in good company.

After a few sips of really good wine, along with some food and entertainment, it was time to go home.

"It was nice meeting you ladies. Have a good night," I said while putting on my jacket.

"Yes, it was great meeting you too. We have a happy hour event this Friday. Hopefully we'll see you there," Joyelle mentioned.

"Yes, for sure," I replied.

I gave the ladies hugs good-bye and walked to my car with a smile on my face, knowing I would be okay.

Over the next couple of months, I had something to do every weekend. I had dinner dates with the girls and happy hour events. I attended plays and concerts and enjoyed different kinds of outdoor activities.

This helped me not focus negatively about my situation with John. We were still married, and he was still not communicating with me. I was in limbo, not knowing what was going on. I just hoped I was giving John the time he needed to come back to this situation whole and with a clear mind.

I decided to purchase a ticket to the Seattle Art Festival at a rustic event hall. I had the perfect dress and shoes to wear. The event started at two o'clock in the afternoon. I knew a few ladies who were planning to attend, so I decided to meet them there.

Of course, I arrived on time. It was a habit. Actually, I was better off when people told me something started later, otherwise I'd always be there before everyone else. I checked in at the registration table at the front door to get my drink and raffle tickets. I walked around the event hall, looking at the various art displays throughout the rustic mosaic-themed room. As people started to arrive, I made my way over to the door to look out for the ladies I anticipated to see at the event.

As I was waiting, I noticed the food buffet was now open. I was hungry but too shy to start eating by myself. Then I noticed a gentleman sitting on the couch who was already eating. I thought, *Perfect! I'll get some food and go sit by him so it doesn't look like I'm the only one eating.*

I put some cocktail meatballs, carrot sticks, and chicken skewers on my small plate and walked toward the man sitting on the couch.

"Hi! Can I sit here?" I politely asked.

"Sure, of course," the gentleman said as he shifted to make more room for me on the couch.

I started eating the meatballs first.

"How did you hear about this event?" the gentleman asked.

"My girlfriend told me about it, and I decided to come and support," I replied.

"That's good."

"What about you?" I asked.

"I know the organizer, so I support her every year."

"Oh, that's nice!"

We chatted back and forth for a few minutes before we asked each other our names.

"My name is Marcus, by the way," he said as he switched his plate from one hand to the other to extend a handshake.

"My name is Justyne." I smiled and completed the handshake.

Marcus was born and raised in Seattle, and he shared a lot of information about things to do in the city. He seemed to enjoy that I was new to the city so he could tell me all the wonderful things about it.

After a while, I looked up and saw my girlfriends walking into the event and heading toward me. We greeted one another with a hug, and I introduced them to Marcus. I thanked him for the conversation and parted ways.

The event included a fashion show, a cigar lounge, and many other activities. I had an awesome time.

As I was getting ready to leave, Marcus approached me once again.

"Hey, can I call you sometime and perhaps show you more of this wonderful city?" Marcus politely asked.

"Sure," I said, then I hesitated, wondering if I should explain my situation. After a moment, I decided it wasn't a good time and place.

We exchanged phone numbers and said our good-byes. I appreciated his friendly approach. I felt seen, valued, and respected in just the few minutes in his presence. Although I wasn't interested in dating, I hoped Marcus would be a friend.

While enjoying Seattle, I still remained in close contact with friends in Houston. Many people were staying hopeful that John and I would reconcile. I truly appreciated my conversations with Michelle. I will always be grateful for how she and Doug opened their home to me after I'd left Cherie's home.

Now Michelle continued to encourage me by reminding me of who God was in this situation. She helped me remain still to allow God to work this out. The closer I got to God, the less I worried. I was reaching a place from where I could really see how John and I could work things out and get back together. It required John to be really honest with himself. If he would do that, then I would be there to go through the process together. I continued to wait for John to reach a place in which we could come together and talk about marriage.

In the meantime, though, I made the most of my new life, which was moving in several exciting directions. A few days after the Arts Festival, Marcus called to ask if I wanted to meet him at a lake to grab some food. I accepted the invitation. We met at Lake Hills to get fish-and-chips at the eatery on-site. It was a beautiful, sunny day to enjoy a conversation by the lake. Marcus continued to tell me more stories about Seattle, and I shared stories about Belleville. We never talked about anything personal. He didn't ask any questions, and neither did I. This was exactly what I needed.

My attention also shifted to my brother and sister-in-law, who were expecting a baby the following month. Since experiencing the loss of my own baby, I'd decided to become a doula. I had started working with a not-for-profit organization providing doula services for low-income families.

The decision to become a doula was truly a voice from God. It healed me in many ways, confronting the pain and disappointment of my tragic loss and transforming it into the joy of giving other women the educational and emotional support I didn't have. And now, I was getting ready to be a doula to help my new niece or nephew enter the world.

Then while working on my computer one day, an email notification popped up. It was from Michael.

Subject: Hi

Hi, Justyne,
Are you by chance in Belleville?

Oh my goodness! I hadn't heard from Michael since our email exchange over a year earlier—the infamous emails that were mysteriously sent to John. I replied, starting a thread.

Subject: Re: Hi

Hi, Michael!
No, I'm not. Are you visiting?

Subject: Re: Hi
Yes. On my way there from NY.

Subject: Re: Hi
Oh no—sorry to have missed you. It would have been nice to connect. If you are ever in Seattle, let me know!

Subject: Re: Hi
Oh, wow! Okay, sure thing. :)

Now, that was a surprise! I had intentionally chosen not to contact Michael and tell him about my situation. I didn't want to make things more confusing, and I wanted to give my marriage an honest effort to be fixed, if it were meant to be fixed. And beyond that, I wanted to be sure it was God—not just me—orchestrating my life. If Michael were to come back into my life, it would have to be divinely ordained and for real this time.

A few weeks later, I received another email from Michael.

Subject: Re: Hi

Looks like I will be in your town on the 31st and the 1st. Any chance of connecting?

Michael was coming to Seattle! However, I was leaving for Vancouver soon. When I replied, I explained the situation. I didn't want Michael to think I didn't want to see him, so I quickly let him know of other opportunities.

Subject: Re: Hi

I'm hopeful and faithful that there will be another time soon. :) Even if you do a stopover in SEA, let me know because I'm minutes away from the airport! Safe travels!

A few days later, I landed in Vancouver safely and waited for my brother to pick me up from the airport. I stayed over two weeks and was side by side with my brother and sister-in-law as they welcomed their son, Dylan, into the world.

While in Vancouver, I sent an email to Michael to ask how he was enjoying Seattle. In his reply, he explained that he had left Seattle a day early, seeing as I wasn't in town. But he had another trip coming up on September 12 with a layover in Seattle. It was only two hours, but he was hoping we could connect. I happily confirmed that the day worked for me.

When I arrived back home from Vancouver on September 9, I anticipated seeing Michael in just a few days. It would be the first time I'd seen him in five years.

16

THE VISIT

September 2015

The day before Michael arrived, I was at work when I received a phone call from my lawyer.

"Hi, Justyne. It's Chris. Is this a good time to talk?"

"Hi, Chris. Yes, it's a good time."

The truth was, anytime Chris called was a good time because I was eager to know how the divorce was proceeding.

"So, we've sent John Black the marriage settlement agreement for the uncontested divorce, but he hasn't responded. We'll have to file a petition and have him served."

"Okay. Let's do what we have to do."

I didn't understand why John was being so unresponsive. It was the most bizarre situation. Not only did he not participate in the marriage but he was now not participating in the divorce.

"All right," Chris replied. "I'll start working on the petition and send it to you for review. I know in the marriage settlement agreement you only asked John to pay off the loan for the restaurant, but I think in this petition you should put everything you are entitled to under Texas law."

I thought about Chris's suggestion. I didn't want anything from John, except for him to take responsibility for what he knew was his responsibility. Filing the petition would cost me a lot more money than I'd anticipated, but at that point, I had no choice. I decided to allow Chris to proceed with putting everything on the petition, in hopes it would alert John to respond to the original settlement agreement. I wasn't prepared for this, but it looked as if it wouldn't be an easy divorce after all.

"That's fine, Chris. I'll look out for your email and respond as soon as possible."

I hung up the phone in confusion, wondering why John was making this difficult.

That night, I logged in to Netflix and watched two movies while thinking about seeing Michael for the first time in five years.

Michael's flight was scheduled to arrive at 7:20 a.m. As I was getting dressed, I checked the flight status and noticed the flight had landed early. I quickly finished slipping into a black jumpsuit and put a cardigan over it. I looked casual but good.

Driving up to the airport parking ramp, I pushed for a ticket in slight annoyance, knowing how expensive parking would be. But I quickly got over it, knowing I was just minutes away from seeing my friend again. My feelings were all over the place. I was happy, excited, nervous, while trying to maintain cool and calm all at the same time. *Will he look the same? Will he be happy to see me? Will he regret the visit?* The truth was, I didn't know what to expect.

I asked security if I could get to the gate to meet Michael right off the plane, but I got the polite no. So I walked to baggage claim to wait for him. I waited about ten minutes until my phone rang.

"Hey! Good morning!" Michael's smile came through in his voice.

"Hey! Good morning, Michael!" I echoed.

"I'm walking down to the exit right now. Where are you?"

"I'm at the baggage claim, in front of the doors. You'll see me when you exit."

"All righty, see you soon!" Michael hung up.

I picked up a magazine to look through. Otherwise, my head would have been bumping up and down as I watched for Michael to come in sight. After about five minutes of diverting my attention, I looked up and saw Michael. I walked toward him so he could see me. When he did, the biggest smile covered his face. Just as I'd remembered him.

"How are you? It's so good to see you," Michael said as he gave me a hug.

"Yes, it's so good to see you too." I embraced him back.

We stood in place for a few moments looking at each other. Michael looked the same, except he had grown out his hair past his neck. He still looked good to me. His personality and energy hadn't changed. Michael still knew how to make me smile.

"So, where should we go?" Michael asked. We had only two hours for his layover, so we planned to just stay at the airport.

"We can sit down at the end of the hall," I said, pointing to an empty area of the baggage terminal.

"Okay, great!" Michael glanced down the hall. "Oh, there's a Starbucks right here. Do you want anything to drink?"

"Yeah, sure. I'll have a hot chocolate." My usual favorite.

I waited for Michael to get our drinks, then we walked together to grab a seat.

"So, how are you?" Michael genuinely asked.

With a timid smile, I responded, "I'm doing pretty good. How are you?"

"I'm good! Same ol', same ol'." He smiled again. "You look good!"

"Really?"

I was taken aback by the compliment. John rarely to never said things to make me feel good about myself.

"Yeah! You really do look good!" Michael insisted.

Michael and I got caught up on each other's work life and our friends and family back home in Belleville. I even showed him a few YouTube videos I thought were pretty funny. We didn't speak about our personal situations. I didn't tell him I was separated, and I didn't ask if he were still engaged.

More than an hour passed, then Michael checked his boarding pass.

"Man, my connecting flight is in an hour. But I'm really enjoying talking to you," he said while looking at his boarding pass in disappointment.

"Yeah, I know. I'm enjoying talking to you too," I replied with a smile.

Michael put his head down for a minute, then raised it back up with a smile and ponder in his eyes. "I really don't want to leave you. I want to spend the whole day with you. What do you have planned for the day?"

"Um, nothing much. I was just going to go back home to finish some work."

"Okay, then. I'm going to see if I can catch a later flight. Can I hang out with you for the day?"

"Of course!"

Michael reached for his phone to search for other flight times later that day. I sat back waiting in anticipation. He was able to get a seat on the last flight out at ten thirty that night.

With that, we got up from our seats and walked toward the parking ramp to leave the airport.

I couldn't believe this was happening. Michael was riding in my car. We were hanging out together. It was as if no time had passed between us. It was the most comfortable I'd been in years.

Our first stop was lunch. Michael and I hadn't eaten all morning, so I went to an organic café I knew he would like. We sat outside on the patio, enjoying sandwiches, lemonade, and more conversation.

Second stop was my apartment. I had to go home for a conference call, and Michael had to log in to his laptop to respond to work emails. As we made our way to my apartment, I felt the need to warn Michael of my minimalist living conditions. When I left Houston, I had just my clothes and a few other belongings. I decided to get a couch, a TV, and a kitchen table to furnish my apartment, but that was it. I tried to explain my move from Houston to Seattle without mentioning the separation.

"I'm sort of in limbo with the direction of my life, so having less is better," I said.

Michael chuckled and gave me a smile to let me know it was okay.

I hadn't yet mentioned John or my marriage, but it was obvious that I was living in the apartment alone—I was sure Michael knew something was up. Thankfully, he was being nice by not asking any questions I wasn't ready to answer.

While Michael was working at the kitchen table, I was at my desk on a conference call. After we were done, we somehow met each other at the couch and started watching TV. I showed him some more funny YouTube videos, and we continued to laugh together.

Our third stop was to a lake. I wanted to show him the beautiful scenery in Seattle. I suggested we take a walk around the lake.

"So, how long is the walking path?" Michael asked in hesitation.

"It's only about five kilometers—about sixty minutes," I said with a chuckle.

We started walking, and suddenly there was a moment of silence. In that moment, I was thinking about asking him questions about his personal life, but I didn't want to make things uncomfortable. So I just continued walking, looking at the lake and trees.

"Hey, why are you so quiet? What are you thinking?" Michael finally asked.

"Are you sure you want to know?" I replied with a laughing smile, as if I had just gotten caught.

"Yeah, I do." He grinned with anticipation.

"Okay . . . are you still engaged?"

Michael laughed in surprise before answering the question. "Well, yeah, kinda." He began to explain. "We've been engaged for a long time, but I'm starting to feel it's not what I want. We're trying to make it work, but I'm thinking it may not be the best thing. What about you? Are you still married?"

"Well, yeah, kinda!" I said. "We're separated right now. I haven't spoken to him in several months. And I just filed for divorce."

We both took a moment to digest the information we received from each other.

"So, what happened?" Michael innocently asked.

"Everything!" I was reluctant to get into the details with Michael because I was realizing marrying John had been a big mistake from the beginning. "It wasn't a good marriage. We didn't get a chance to build a foundation for the relationship. I ended up leaving because things got so bad. We haven't spoken all year. I don't know if things will be reconciled. He would need to acknowledge everything that has happened and be honest about a lot of things he hasn't been honest about. And I'm not sure if he's ready to do that." I purposely avoided saying John's name.

"Oh, wow. Sorry to hear that. It's really unfortunate." Michael sounded sincere. "I remembered when I heard you were getting married. I paced back and forth in my house like a million times. I was like, 'Whoa, Justyne is getting married.'" Michael drifted away in his thoughts.

"So, how about you? Why are you having second thoughts about your engagement?" I asked to continue the conversation.

"I've just realized a lot of things about her that I don't think will be a good fit. I don't trust her decision-making ability, and it seems as though she still needs to get her life together first," Michael honestly replied. He too seemed to avoid using her name.

We continued walking, allowing the conversation to shift in any direction it needed to go. We were mesmerized by the beautiful homes along the lakefront. Before we knew it, we'd completed the full path.

Our fourth stop was to get dinner before Michael's flight. We found an authentic Thai restaurant just a block away from the lake.

"Thank you for the day. I can't believe we spent the whole day together," Michael expressed while taking a bite of his food.

"Yes, I really enjoyed it too. We've spent, like, twelve hours together!"

"Yeah, that's so cool!"

We both smiled and put our heads down to take a few more bites of our food. It was amazing that five years seemed like no time at all.

Our fifth stop was back to the airport for Michael to catch the last flight out. The drive to the airport was a bit sober. We were in our own thoughts, thinking about the amazing day we had shared and not knowing when we'd see each other again. I decided to park in the ramp so I could walk Michael to check-in and spend a few more moments with him.

"So, what do you have planned for the rest of the week?" Michael asked as he organized his laptop bag and carry-on luggage.

"Nothing much. Just work and hanging out with friends. What about you?"

"Just work, then I fly back home to Atlanta on Friday. I'll give you a call when I land in San Francisco," Michael assured me.

"Okay, sounds good."

We gave each other a hug and said good-bye.

On my way home, I received a text from Michael:

> Hi, Justyne. It's Michael. I feel like the pants I'm wearing are about to burst. :) I had a fantastic time with you. Thank you for everything!

I replied to the text:

> LOL . . . That's what happens when you wear tight pants and eat too much food! Just don't bend down! I had an amazing time with you too. :) Thank you for taking the time!

I slept well that night. My heart felt at ease.

A few weeks later, I was home when I received a call from my lawyer.

"Hi, Chris," I anxiously responded.

"I wanted to provide you an update on our progress in trying to serve your husband," he said. "The process server went to the house, and the person who answered the door said John no longer lives there."

"WHAT?" My eyes and mouth widely opened.

"The man who answered the door might have been his father. So, I don't think it's true that John is no longer living there. But it's clear that he's avoiding being served. This is quite common, so don't worry," Chris tried to calmly reassure me. "We will get him."

I was completely out of words. I didn't know what to do.

"Okay," I eventually said.

"Don't worry, Justyne. We'll get him," Chris assured me again before hanging up.

I decided to go to bed at five o'clock in the afternoon. The fear and doubt were too heavy to enjoy the rest of the day.

17

THE DISCOVERY

October 2015

Despite all the craziness John was putting me through, I was amazed at the attitude I had developed about the situation. I posted words of affirmation along my standing mirror to remind myself of self-control, patience, and love. I also posted prayers to focus on the true purpose of the battle I was going through. The whole situation was absolutely crazy for no reason. John's evident immaturity truly blew my mind. But I had to remember to keep calm and centered and allow God to do what He needed to do.

One day when I opened my mailbox, about ten envelopes from the IRS filled the space. These were the tax return receipts I had requested. John had always filed our taxes jointly as a married couple, but I had no record of what was filed. He'd never shared any information about our taxes. So, I decided to find out for myself.

I walked back to my apartment, sat on the couch, and opened each envelope one by one. The first envelope was the tax return receipt for 2012. All looked okay. The second envelope was the tax return receipt for 2013. Again, everything looked okay. John's income was slightly higher than I had thought, but it could have been overtime.

The third envelope was the tax return receipt for 2014. My hands dropped the paper. John had made over $180,000 that year.

WHAT THE HELL?

My heart started to race. Instantly, I was devastated. I'd thought his salary was $85,000 a year.

In 2014, I lost my job and started devoting myself to the restaurant full-time. I was never paid for my work or effort at the restaurant, nor did my husband ever give me money to buy something for myself.

John had always made it seem as if he didn't have any money. Before I lost my job, I contributed money into our checking account for bills, and I added about $10,000 to our savings account. But sometimes John didn't deposit money into the joint account, so I had to transfer money from savings into checking to cover the bills.

My heart sank thinking about my husband's deception, greed, and coldness. I was disgusted. I had given so much to him, effortlessly. It truly hurt to realize he hadn't given anything at all.

I could barely open the other envelopes. They were summaries of the restaurant tax filing, which apparently was in my name. I became more and more disturbed as information revealed itself to me—John didn't tell me he had associated my name to the business in the tax documents.

I was so upset that I went straight to bed to sleep off the gnawing feeling in the pit of my stomach.

The next day, I decided to call Peter, John's best man at our wedding, to get some help.

"Hi, Justyne!" Peter greeted me, seeing my name come up on his phone.

"Hey, Peter. How are you doing? I know it's been a while. I've tried not to call you because I get the sense that you don't want to be involved in the situation with me and John," I honestly said.

"Yeah, I understand. But it's not like I don't want to be involved—I just don't know how I can help. But I've been thinking about you and praying for you, wondering how you are doing. I know it must be tough not knowing and being in limbo," Peter expressed.

"Yes, it has been tough. Well, here is an update: One of the deacons at the church spoke to John, and John told the deacon that he didn't see us reconciling anytime soon. I eventually had to file for divorce because John has been unresponsive," I explained. "My lawyer tried to serve him the divorce papers, but his father answered the door saying John doesn't live at the house anymore."

"Oh, man. I'm sorry to hear that."

"Have you spoken to John?" I asked, hoping to get any insight.

"Yeah, but whenever I speak to him, he doesn't talk about y'all's situation," he said matter-of-factly.

"Okay. I'm just trying to figure out what to do here. Can you find out what John is doing?"

Peter hesitated. "I don't know . . . I don't want to get involved in a divorce situation."

"What? All I'm asking is for you to have a man-to-man talk with your friend to understand why he's behaving the way he is. He's been unresponsive, and when he spoke to Deacon Patrick, he told him I was manipulative and that he had no intentions of reconciling. So, why is he avoiding the divorce if he doesn't want the marriage?" My voice got sterner with each sentence.

"Well, first let me say this," Peter said in a deep and steady voice. "I'm not going to allow you to speak about John without him here to defend himself—"

I interrupted to correct the nonsense coming from Peter. "I'm not talking 'bad' about John. I'm telling you exactly what happened— what the deacon told me. I'm telling you the facts of the situation and what he did." I was officially annoyed.

"Well, he still needs to defend himself. What I gather from my conversation with John is that he's spiritually unsure of what he needs to do. I can't tell you exactly what he said, but my sense is that he doesn't know."

"So, can you talk to him to find out why he isn't saying anything to me? Why he hasn't responded to the divorce?" I was desperate for help.

"Sorry," Peter replied. "I won't speak to John for you. I don't want to get involved in a divorce situation," he admitted. "I've spent more time than I intended to on the phone already. I have to go."

"Okay, good-bye." I hung up.

I went through my contacts and deleted Peter's number from my phone. Peter was John's best man at our wedding, yet his reluctance to hold his friend accountable was disturbing. Peter knew that John didn't open the door when I went to visit him at the house in Seattle months earlier. Yet Peter said nothing to John. Peter knew that John hadn't talked to me about the status of our marriage. Yet Peter said nothing to John. Now Peter knew that John was facing divorce and had his family lying about his whereabouts. Yet Peter still decided to say nothing to John.

The cowardliness and ignorance were infuriating. In one breath, Peter said he was praying for us, and in another breath, he said he couldn't help.

Hypocrite.

The weeks ahead were intense as my anxiety increased. I didn't know what to do.

Every couple of weeks, Michael and I would exchange a few text messages and phone calls, but we kept things very casual. We respected the situations we were both in. Michael was engaged and wanted to give it a really good try. And I was still married. We both recognized that anything could happen.

Sometimes in moments of anxiety, I confided in Michael. He provided encouragement, trying to get me to think positive. However, I kept trying to tell him he didn't know how bad things were.

I decided it was time to contact Nicole, John's ex-wife. I had never met her because John spoke so horribly about her and did everything he could to keep me from talking to her. But now it was time I knew the truth.

I logged in to Facebook and found her profile. I knew her name from looking up the public court records on their dissolution of marriage case. I clicked the messenger icon to send her a message.

> Hi, Nicole. Hope you are well! This is Justyne (John's soon-to-be ex-wife). I've been wanting to reach out to you for a while to connect. Please let me know if we'll be able to speak tonight. Thanks!

The next day, I logged back into Facebook. No response. I sent another message.

> Hi, Nicole. Also, can you please keep my reaching out to you confidential between me and you? I hope to hear from you. Thank you!

Days went by, and I didn't receive a response. I figured I had at least tried.

It was 5:30 a.m. Tuesday when my phone rang, waking me out of my sleep. I rolled over to see who was calling. It was John's number.

"Hello," I answered in my barely awake voice.

"Hi," John responded without identifying himself.

"How are you doing?" I started the conversation.

"I'm doing fine."

"That's good."

"I know we haven't spoken. I didn't have your information and didn't have your address. I just got your phone number," John quickly said to start the conversation.

"Really?" I knew he was lying.

"I know we have a lot to talk about, but something has come up that I need to talk to you about. I was speaking to my daughter's mom, and she told me that you reached out to her."

"Yes, I did," I confirmed while covering up the surprise in my voice. I never thought Nicole would say anything to John, given their strained relationship.

"Why did you contact her? You don't see me contacting people from your past. Why are you bringing my daughter into this?"

"*What?*" I had to be aware of how John was trying to twist the situation around. "No one is bringing your daughter into anything. You don't even know why I reached out to Nicole. You don't even know what you are talking about." My voice started to rise.

"So, why did you contact her? Don't talk to her."

"Listen—I've been trying to contact you for months, and you have been unresponsive. And now you suddenly call me to talk about me reaching out to your ex-wife? Are you *serious?*"

"Okay, there are a few things I do want to talk to you about. And now that I have your phone number, I will call you to talk about them."

"Or you can respond to the many emails I sent you," I retorted.

"I'll text you," John childishly responded.

"Whatever."

"And let me make myself clear: do not speak to my ex-wife," John aggressively said.

I hung up.

I looked at my phone in complete shock about the four-minute-and-twenty-five-second conversation I'd just had with John.

My phone rang again. It was John calling back.

"Hi. I don't want to lose focus on the matter at hand . . ." John continued his argument.

"Okay . . ."

"Don't call my ex-wife. I'm telling you—do not talk to her," John aggressively stated, even though he sounded nervous at the same time.

"I look forward to receiving the things you would like to talk about!" I spoke loudly, ignoring what John had said, then I hung up.

He didn't want to lose focus on the matter at hand? We were still married. He was unresponsive to my many attempts to contact him. Divorce papers had been filed. Yet he thought the matter at hand was me sending his ex-wife a Facebook message.

I was extremely bothered. I didn't understand the logic in John's thinking. It was bizarre.

Later that day, I received a call from Michelle in Houston.

"Hey, Sis. How are you? Is this a good time to talk?" Michelle asked.

"Yes, I'm good!" I replied.

"I just received a call from John," she said outright.

"What?"

"Yes, I know. I was surprised too. I've known John for many years, and he's never called me," Michelle said with a laugh. "So, he told me you reached out to his ex-wife, and he's very concerned about that. He said he has finally calmed down and is no longer angry, but he thinks something like this will create more problems."

"*What?*" I repeated. My mouth fell open. "At any point, did he acknowledge that we are still married?" Once again, I couldn't understand John's disregard of the real issues.

"Yes. He definitely acknowledged the marriage. He said you all needed a break right now. I tried to tell him that I didn't think you had any ill intentions for contacting his ex-wife. I said sometimes when we women haven't received any communication at all, we resort to desperation to get clarity. Well, he almost took my head off with that comment. He started saying, 'Oh, you don't know Justyne.'" She paused. "If it's taken him this long to not be angry anymore, then I think it's going take to him a lot longer to acknowledge the truth about what happened."

I absorbed everything Michelle told me. "What did he mean, 'You don't know Justyne'? He doesn't know me much more," I said.

I was slowly understanding how dishonest John had been with me throughout our entire marriage. And then for him to say "You don't know Justyne" seemed so disillusioned.

"Sis, you've been doing good so far. Don't lose your faith in this. Just be aware of your interactions with this ex-wife. Let God do what He needs to do in this situation," Michelle advised.

"Yes, I understand. I'm not going to reach out to his ex again. Especially since she went back to John and said something." I felt defeated.

Michelle and I said our good-byes. I went out to dinner with friends that night to avoid being at home alone, thinking about what had happened.

It was now Friday, just a few days after receiving John's 5:30 a.m. call. I was at work when I noticed a message pop up from Facebook. It was Nicole.

> Justyne, Josephine and I have been missing you for a long time. Yes, you can reach out to me privately. Here is my number 999-555-8965. I'm so glad to know you are okay! Josephine is really worried.
>
> Just text me if you'd like. I'm soooooo relieved to hear from you. You just have no idea how this settles my heart.

What in the world? I didn't know what to think. Nicole had told John I had reached out to her, yet now in her message she was saying I could talk to her privately. I didn't respond.

One day passed when I received another message from Nicole.

> I have been praying for you during a twenty-day church campaign. I'm really hoping that speaking to me can bring healing to your heart and some closure for you. Josephine is well, growing in grace and more beautiful than ever.

Nicole sent me updated pictures of Josephine. Once again, I didn't respond to the messages. I needed time to think about how and whether I would respond.

That weekend, I was glad to have my girlfriend Marie and her daughter come for a visit. I still kept in touch with many of the friends I made in Houston, and Marie was one of them. Christian author and inspirational speaker Joyce Meyers was in Seattle on her conference tour, so we decided to make a weekend out of it. The timing was perfect.

Saturday morning while I was preparing breakfast for me and my guests, I received a phone call from John.

"Hello," I answered in surprise.

"Hello. I know I said I would call you to let you know about things we need to discuss, but I'm going to forgo that since you're already on another path. And I'll just deal with the consequences."

"What are you talking about? What consequences?"

"Well, you're talking to my ex—"

"Listen," I interrupted. "I'm not going to talk about your ex-wife. If this is why you called, then I'm sorry, but we are not going to talk about at that. You are missing the point."

"What's the point?" he calmly said.

"The point is that we are still married and you've said nothing. You haven't responded to my attempts to contact you. Now we're in the midst of a divorce, and you're still saying nothing. I think we need a mediator to discuss this issue."

"Okay," John said abruptly.

"Okay? Okay, you want to see a mediator?" I repeated to make sure I'd heard him correctly. I was taken back by his complacency.

"Yes."

"Okay," I said.

I hesitated. I was about to offer to schedule the mediation session, yet I was still mad. Many times, I had tried to contact John, but he was just unresponsive. For once, I wanted him to do something to show he really wanted to work through this. Then again, I was still trying to remain open to the process and to the chance of reconciliation. So I decided I should take the lead in setting up a mediation.

"Here's what I'll do. I'm in Seattle, and I attend a church here. I'll contact the church to set up a time for us."

As soon as I finished the sentence, John hung up.

Later that afternoon, I took Marie and her daughter to Westfield Southcenter mall to hang out. I received another message from Nicole.

> Sent you a few messages. Hope you're okay.

I decided to respond this time—I truly wanted to know what she had to say.

> Hey, Nicole—Sorry for the delay . . . Thanks for the messages! It means a lot. I'm going to call you tomorrow afternoon.

I planned to call Nicole the next day after my guests left. I thought about how to approach the conversation. Being honest was my conclusion. I would let Nicole know I was aware that she'd told John I had reached out to her. I would see where the conversation went from there.

For the time being, I focused my attention back on my guests. This was turning out to be an awesome girlfriend visit. I was so excited for the company.

We decided to catch a matinee at the mall. We got our tickets, entered the theater, and took our seats. Just then, I felt a vibration from my phone. I checked it and saw a very long Facebook message from Nicole. I decided to read it later.

We spent half the day at the mall, then we went to dinner at a local restaurant. When we were all seated, I pulled out my phone to read Nicole's message.

> I think that there is a lot you don't know. And I'm hoping it will help you heal. I'm sorry to hear you are divorcing. As you know, my divorce from John is currently still in court—although finalized, he still takes me to court for child custody issues. It takes my breath away, and it's very strange.

When we married, we were so young. We never were intimate until after we married, and I got pregnant with Josephine on my first cycle. So we married in February and were pregnant in March. After that, he wanted nothing to do with me or the pregnancy. I was his wife, but he never told his parents, and he re-signed a lease with his roommate, forcing me to find a place of my own. He wasn't even there to help me move in.

Within two weeks of moving back to Houston . . . alone . . . I went into preterm labor at twenty-six weeks. I had to call John at his apartment to take me to the hospital. While there, he asked, "How long is this going to take? I have to see my advisor in the morning." When the hospital cleared us to go home, he drove me back to my apartment around 8:00 a.m.

He had hardly left when I began to bleed. I couldn't find him. My sister was in town for the holiday and rushed me back to the ER. Within that short forty-five-minute time frame, I had dilated to four centimeters. John finally showed up hours later.

They were able to stop my contractions for eight days, but I had Josephine at twenty-seven weeks. Again, John could not be found, so I birthed Josephine alone, twenty years old, via C-section. He still declined to tell his family, even though Josephine required seven blood transfusions. My family all have Rh-negative blood, but Josephine carried John's blood type, which is Rh-positive. She was critical for a very long time. During this time, John was distant, not wanting to visit the baby, and he was no comfort or helpmate to me.

Finally, I asked him to separate. We had one last visit a couple of weeks later. We mutually agreed to divorce.

Josephine remained a secret to his family until she was almost six years old. I never met his parents until her sixth birthday party.

I do not believe John is a bad man. He just struggles with the truth. I could never understand why he would hide me or Josephine. He told me you wanted to speak to me before you both married, but he wouldn't give you my number. I don't understand John at all.

He finally told Josephine about the loss of your son in July during a therapy session. She wept uncontrollably, saying, "I had a brother?" I wept and fell before the Lord as well when I got home. My heart ached upon the news and for Josephine to be kept in a guessing mode for so long.

Everyone grieves differently. If there is anything I can do or answer any questions, I'm here.

FYI, he told the child psychiatrist and Josephine that you got a job offer out of town, and that's why you haven't been seen.

I can't say that I ever loved John. I never got the opportunity. Our divorce dragged out for almost two and a half years because he kept insisting we could make it work. We even went to court on two separate occasions and had our divorce dismissed. Neither of us dated seriously for eight years after our divorce.

I would've loved the opportunity to have at least met you before you both married. And Josephine deserved that too. To this day, she's never been the same because she wasn't involved in the wedding.

> She says it was the worst day of her life as she cried from the front row watching her cousins and your goddaughters participate. It really, really hurt her.
>
> People can change. I don't hate John, and this is no John-bashing session. I just thought it is only fair that you knew the truth. God saw that I was unloved by my husband.

I could barely eat the food I'd ordered. I didn't share the message with Marie, but I did let her know it wasn't good. Marie had known John before I did, and she started to share some information she found odd about him, like how he was very adamant about Josephine not speaking to anyone at the church when she came to visit. It was so extreme that John even approached Marie's daughter after seeing the two girls together. He asked Marie's daughter if Josephine had given her her phone number and if so to delete it.

I started to wonder, *Who did I marry?*

After dropping Marie and her daughter at the airport, I went to the grocery store. I waited until six o'clock in the evening to call Nicole. The first time I called, I got her voice mail. A few minutes later, I called a second time and got voice mail again. I decided to send her a Facebook message letting her know I was trying to get a hold of her. Within a half hour, she responded, letting me know she had been taking a nap and that I could call her now.

Ring, ring.

"Hi, Nicole. It's Justyne."

"Hi, Justyne! Well, it is very nice to finally speak to you!" Nicole graciously said in the politest voice.

"Thank you! Same to you." I remembered my plan to be up front with her. "I must say, I was hesitant to respond to you or even call you, because John said you had told him about me reaching out to you."

"What? I haven't spoken to John," Nicole said, shocked. "Honey, when I responded to you on Facebook, it was the first time I saw the message. I don't speak to John like that. I didn't tell him anything."

204 • FAITH TO STRENGTH

Nicole sounded genuinely sincere—it was hard not to believe her. But that left me confused.

"Well, I don't understand," I said. "How else would he know I'd reached out to you?"

"Wait—John is calling me right now." I could tell she was checking her phone at the same time. "Does he know we are talking right now?" she asked with anxiety.

Then it hit me: John must have had access to my Facebook account. He had seen all the messages I had sent Nicole, including the one right before we started talking. Perhaps I had logged in to my Facebook account while on his computer once, and he had saved my password. Immediately, I logged in to Facebook to change my password.

"He must have access to my Facebook account," I explained. "I just changed my password right now."

"Oh, that is scary. That means he read that long message I wrote to you. That may cause problems for me," Nicole responded with concern. But then she quickly brushed it off. "But who cares?"

We continued to talk for two hours and forty-four minutes. I listened to every word.

Nicole went into more detail about the experiences she mentioned in her Facebook message. As she spoke, I couldn't help but notice the similarities in our relationships with John.

John wasn't present when his daughter was born prematurely. John wasn't present when his son was born prematurely. Both Nicole and I faced emotional, stressful moments with John during our pregnancies. Her daughter lived. My son died. John remained distant in both situations.

Also, John's sisters interfered with his marriage to Nicole the same way they interfered with mine. When Nicole was first pregnant, one of John's sisters actually told Nicole to abort the baby, saying she could have a "real" baby later. His sister even told John that the baby wasn't his and that Nicole was just trying to trap him. This led John to ask Nicole for a paternity test right after Josephine was born prematurely. Years later, John's family continued to shape his opinions and perceptions about Nicole and his daughter.

In my situation, Blossom moved into our home without me knowing or agreeing to a plan. Blossom's presence in our lives shortly into our marriage was the end of any hopes of John and me learning how to build a relationship grounded on mutual trust, respect, and love. She became a crutch and a protection for him to not bond and cleave unto his wife.

John allowed his sisters to manipulate and control his thinking and life. What they thought was right was actually very wrong. It was very clear John didn't know who he was apart from what his sisters told him. His family had enabled his immaturity and bad behavior since the beginning. John didn't know how to stand on his own as a man, father, and husband.

18

THE ATTEMPT

November 2015

Two weeks later, my lawyer called to give me a status update on the attempts to serve John with the divorce petition papers. Earlier, I had sent Chris an email providing potential dates, times, and locations to help find John. Chris told me the process server didn't follow the guidelines and instead went to the business and home when John wasn't there. However, his family was present to tell the process server that John was no longer around.

I told my lawyer to hold off on trying to serve John until November 18. I'd found out that John was suing one of the cooks at the restaurant and had a court appearance. I knew the exact location of where John would be that day. Plus, John had agreed to attend a mediation session, which we could perhaps schedule before November 18. I figured I would have a better understanding of the situation by then.

I spoke with the counselor at church about dates and times for mediation. I then called John so he could confirm which worked best for him. I called multiple times, but there was no answer. I decided to send a text.

> Hi. I'm not sure why you are not answering the phone, but I just wanted to let you know that the counselor provided the following dates and times to meet next week: Wednesday or Thursday at 3:30. Please let me know which will work best for you.

Twelve hours later, John finally replied.

> Neither time works that well. But I could do a video conference on Thursday.

I couldn't believe this. I replied shortly after.

> The request was for us to "come in." I will have to take time off work to attend. If you are serious about this, you will have to make an effort to attend as well and make it a priority.

I didn't receive a response until the next morning.

> My schedule is what it is. Give me the counselor's info, and I'll touch base with them.

I sent John the counselor's contact information. Then a week passed without hearing from John. I left a voice mail with the counselor to confirm whether we were still able to meet on Thursday. Later that day, I received an email from the counselor.

Subject: Scheduling

Hi, Justyne,
I heard from John yesterday afternoon, and he is not able to make a face-to-face meeting for several weeks. We can reschedule to another date if you like. A Skype call, which he asked for, is not recommended.
Continued prayers.

I didn't contact John. I decided to leave it in his hands if he truly wanted to have this meeting.

Two days later, I received a call from Chris.

"Well, some interesting things have happened," he said. "I guess the process server felt bad that he didn't follow your initial email on when to try to serve John. So, he took it upon himself to go to the restaurant and try. And he got him."

"*What!* Oh my goodness!" I felt my heartbeat racing in excitement.

"Yes, we got him. It wasn't a pleasant service. John wasn't cooperative. But he's been officially served with the divorce petition, and he has twenty days to respond. If he doesn't respond, we can look into the process for a default judgment."

"Okay, thank you. I am so happy right now!"

I was surprised by how happy and relieved I felt. It wasn't that I was happy because we were closer to divorce. I was happy because it was *clarity*. After several months of not knowing what was going on, I suddenly had some sense of the direction this marriage was going. Whether good or bad, it was clarity and something John had to respond to.

The following Tuesday, I received a text from John while at work.

> Maybe you've heard, but I called the church and heard back from the counselor a few days later. The counselor was planning a one-time session. Don't know if that's what you had in mind, or if you want more.

John didn't mention being served the divorce papers. I replied with the same lack of acknowledgment.

> I received an email from the counselor on November 8 saying that she spoke to you the day before and that you were not able to make a face-to-face meeting for several weeks. I didn't hear back from you, nor was the meeting rescheduled for another day/time. The meeting was intended to be a one-time occurrence to discuss the state of where things are; we would then determine if additional sessions were needed.

John replied in five minutes.

> She knows I'll reply with dates later. You can find another counselor who will do a teleconference until I can do a face-to-face session.

Of course John had to defend himself to make sure he wasn't in the wrong. Too bad it was a lie. In her email to me, the counselor had never mentioned John agreeing to provide dates at a later time. It was his word against hers, and I had no reason to believe he was telling the truth. Did John think I would continue doing cartwheels for him to attend a counseling meeting to discuss our marriage, which he clearly had no interest in?

I replied, maintaining calm. It began a thread of texts.

> JUSTYNE: I think it would be better for you to find a counselor who will accommodate your situation/schedule. My schedule is flexible, and I will make time for whatever works best for you.

> JOHN: Well, my schedule isn't flexible. Just tell me what you come up with.

> JUSTYNE: Sorry. I can't accept that. People make time for things they want to make time for. I've already made the effort to schedule counseling meetings on two different occasions. You are able to look up counselors and contact them on your own time. (That is not a luxury.) The ball is truly in your court. You can do whatever you are willing to do. Take care.

> JOHN: Reality is, you're the one who's flexible. Not me. There's nothing to "accept." Have a good day.

John was the last person who should mention reality. How did my saying I had a flexible schedule translate into my having to be the one to search for a counselor who did teleconferences because John was unwilling to invest himself in the face-to-face mediation process?

I looked online for ways to respond to defensive people. After reading a few articles while eating my lunch, I decided to respond to John's last message.

> I didn't mean to sound critical, harsh, or insensitive. (Not sure how you feel or felt.) The challenge is your schedule as well as your wanting to do a teleconference (which most counselors won't do, especially for a first meeting). You will have to speak to the counselor to explain your situation. Perhaps you can reach out to the church you attend in Seattle to see if they are willing to assist. I hope that helps.

I didn't receive any more messages from John.

Time went by as I waited through the twenty-day period to see if John would file a response to the divorce petition. I had waited so long to get answers from John; I was eager to finalize this process and move on with my life.

The twenty-day period ended on a Friday in December. I waited until Tuesday to call Chris to discuss next steps. Chris revealed that John did respond to the petition, filing it on Friday, the last day. However, then Chris explained how John responded to the petition—in that he didn't respond to it. He basically answered "NA," or "not applicable," to the whole petition, even to our marriage date and to the number of children.

I shook my head while listening. "Why would someone respond like that?" I asked.

Chris shared his thoughts. "I think John just doesn't know what he's doing or what he wants."

"But even if he doesn't want the divorce, he can still admit the date of marriage and that we have no children," I added.

The next day, I received a text from John stating that the counselor at his church was booked for two months. She referred him to some colleagues, but they hadn't replied yet. He said he hoped to set up a mediation session by the end of the year. Again, there was no mention of the petition or his response.

Chris tried to reach out to John to discuss settlement, but of course, John didn't answer the phone. Since John was attempting to schedule a counseling appointment by the end of year, I told Chris to hold off from contacting John. We had a hearing scheduled in January anyway that John had to attend.

I packed my bags to get ready to spend the holidays in Belleville. I knew that if John were to actually schedule this counseling appointment during that time, I'd have to attend by teleconference as well. I didn't let it bother me and figured I'd wait to hear from John.

I landed in Belleville a week before Christmas so I could spend as much time as possible with my family. My brother and his new family were traveling from Vancouver to spend a week in Belleville as well. I was excited to spend time with my new nephew. This would be the best holiday I'd had in years. Since marrying John, each holiday had been a miserable experience. I looked forward to being happy this holiday by enjoying it with family and friends.

There were moments when I would think maybe John would travel to Belleville to see me and make things better. He hoped to have a counseling meeting set up before the end of the year, which perhaps meant he would see me in person to work it out.

These thoughts about reconciliation surprised me. I was truly at a place of forgiveness and wholeness. I knew the situation was out of my hands, yet I remained willing to go through whatever process it required. I was okay with working things out with John, if he were willing to confront the issues and be truthful with a lot of things he had been dishonest about. On the other hand, I was okay with following through with the divorce, because then I would know what I was divorcing. There were two trains—one called divorce and the other called reconciliation—and John had the ability to start or stop either one.

While I was in Belleville, I received a text from Marie telling me the restaurant was closed.

What?

I asked Marie to call me immediately.

"Hey, girl," she said. "I'm right outside the restaurant, and there is a sign that says 'Sorry, we're closed,' and the chairs are placed on top of the tables."

"Really?" I asked. "Maybe they had an event there last night, and that's why the chairs are up. It's the holidays, so maybe there was a Christmas party."

I tried to think of other possibilities—anything but the restaurant being closed for good. John was so prideful that I didn't think he could actually come to terms with selling the restaurant.

"I'll send John a text to ask him if I can book an event," Marie said. "I'll see what he says." She was so helpful in getting to the truth of the matter.

"Okay!" I laughed at her private investigation aspirations, then hung up the phone.

I reflected on what I knew about the state of the restaurant. John had stopped making payments on the $80,000 loan he'd taken from me to start the restaurant. The bank stopped receiving payments in September, around the time I had the escalated conversation with Debbie and the time when John received the marital settlement agreement papers. I started to fear the possibility of John refusing to pay off the loan, leaving me with the debt. Was John this callous and crooked?

After Christmas, I received a Facebook message from Larry, one of the former employees from the restaurant.

> Hey, what's up? Merry Christmas! Sorry it's late, but I hope you have a very happy and prosperous New Year. I hope you are doing well. Me, I'm hanging in there. Ooh, by the way—the restaurant is closed for good.

I immediately called Larry when I saw the message. My heart starting racing.

"Hey, Larry. I just got your message. How do you know for sure the restaurant is closed?"

"Well, all the paintings on the wall have been taken off, the grease trap that was outside is gone, and I see new people in there now."

Larry had always been honest with me, so I believed him. We spoke for a few minutes more. When I got off the phone, I felt defeated once again.

I logged on my computer and sent John an email.

Subject: Restaurant Permanently Closed

John,
It's come to my attention that the restaurant is permanently closed.
Payments to the loan have not been made since September 2015.
Will the final payment of the loan be reconciled with the closing of the restaurant?
Thanks,
Justyne

I sent Marie a text to let her know her earlier speculation about the closing had been right. She filled me in on her PI work. When she asked about booking an event, John first said he would check the schedule and get back to her. He later replied, saying he had no time available for an event, but he didn't say he was closed. Marie followed her instincts and eventually sent John a text asking outright if the restaurant was closed.

John replied:

We're not open Mondays, and we're closed until the end of the year.

We both knew he was lying.

I contacted Chris to discuss next steps to prevent John from selling the restaurant without my awareness, seeing as it was a marital asset. The divorce petition clearly stated he was not to dispose of any marital assets. At this point, I didn't know how much I could do. It was becoming clear that John felt he could do whatever he wanted.

Chris advised to do a motion of enforcement and injunction against John to produce accounting records for the restaurant. I agreed and allowed him to proceed.

I tried to enjoy the rest of my time in Belleville. My girlfriend Allison and her husband invited me out for New Year's to attend a church concert. I wore a new dress.

The pastor spoke about 2016 being the year of divine visitation, the year God would divinely meet your needs. I had already felt in my spirit that 2016 would be the year of completion, the year God would bring things to completion for my life. I had spent so many years in wonder, anticipation, and disappointment that I had to believe the new year would bring all that to an end. I had to believe that everything that had happened was all to prepare me for what God was bringing in the new year. The pastor's message aligned with what was already in my spirit. I had to believe that everything would be okay.

In 2015, I'd taken a step back by separating from John and living out of a suitcase while staying with friends. But I'd also made a big leap forward in moving to Seattle, reestablishing my career, starting my doula business, and creating a life of peace and happiness. The truth behind the secrets John had kept throughout our marriage was also revealed to me. My big leap forward was clarity and getting myself back.

After two weeks in Belleville, I returned home to Seattle to get ready for work the next morning. I didn't receive a message from John about the counseling session he had hoped to schedule by the end of the year. I also didn't receive a response to the email about the restaurant closing. A court date to hear the status of the divorce was scheduled for the next week.

I anticipated receiving more clarity after the year of limbo John had kept me in.

19

THE TRUTH

January 2016

It was late Monday night. The court hearing with John was scheduled for ten o'clock the next morning. While in bed, I decided to check the online court records. I periodically checked online to see the status of my case and when things had been filed. On this random check, I noticed John had filed a motion to dismiss the petition for divorce. I knew my lawyer wasn't aware of this, or he would have mentioned it. I sent him a quick email at one o'clock in the morning.

Subject: Motion to dismiss

Hi, Chris—
I looked online and noticed John filed a motion to dismiss petition on 1/6. Not sure what grounds he has to do that, but I wanted to give you the heads-up.
Thanks,
Justyne

I couldn't sleep. I repeatedly got up to turn on the television, then go back to bed, then watch videos on my phone. I was restless.

Why would John file a motion to dismiss the petition for divorce and not say anything about stopping the process? The awkward silence made no sense. I felt butterflies in my stomach. I wanted to know the answers right then, at that moment. I looked back and forth at my phone, wishing it to be ten o'clock. I don't know how, but somehow I eventually fell asleep.

No more than an hour or two after closing my eyes, my alarm clock rang. It was time to get ready for work.

I headed to the office to put in a few hours of work before the hearing. I had reserved time in my calendar to go into a conference room at ten to attend the hearing via phone. Chris had told me this hearing would mostly be a status update and would take only a few minutes.

But ten o'clock came and went, and there was no call. At about ten thirty, my phone finally rang. I got up from my desk and walked into a conference room to take the call.

"Hi, Chris," I answered.

"Hi, Justyne. So, the hearing is done."

"Okay," I said with a little surprise. I'd assumed I'd take part in the hearing too, but I trusted Chris's ability to handle it on my behalf. "How did it go? Did John show up?"

"Yes, he was there." Chris paused. "So, this case has taken an interesting turn." He paused again. "John produced a divorce judgment he got back in June."

"WHAT?"

My heart raced.

"Apparently, John started a divorce petition back in April last year and received a default judgment against you because you didn't respond. He claims he had no way of getting in contact with you. So that would explain why he responded 'NA' to the petition—he had already finalized the divorce."

I had no words. So many thoughts rushed through my mind. I was in complete shock.

Chris continued in my silence. "The next step here is to review the documents he filed last year. He claims he's open to a settlement and that he'll call the office to discuss."

Still I said nothing.

Chris tried to reassure me in the midst of my few words. "I know this is a shocker. I'm shocked as well. Over my twenty-five years of experience, I've never seen something like this before. But don't worry—we'll get this straighten out."

I didn't want the call to be over. I wanted to keep Chris on the phone until I understood what had just happened. But then I realized I was paying for every minute of the call.

After hanging up, I sat in the conference room. My heart was still racing, and many thoughts were going through my head. I had to talk to someone. I had to talk to someone. I *had* to talk to someone.

I called Michelle. No answer.

I called Michael. No answer.

I had to talk to someone. I had to talk to someone.

I sent Michael a text. No answer.

I called Michelle again. No answer.

I called Deacon Patrick. No answer.

I couldn't call my mom. I was too upset. And I knew she would be more upset than I was.

The phone rang. It was Michael.

"Hey, what's up?" he asked.

"Oh my gosh!" I blurted. "I think I'm going to cry right now. Hold on—I need to take a deep breath."

"Oh no! What's happened?" Michael asked with worry.

"So," I began, "I know I haven't talked much about my divorce situation. But John was served with the papers, and we had a court date today. My lawyer attended, and he just called me to say that John already got the divorce *back in June*."

"What? How is that possible?" Michael asked in shock.

"He told the courts he had no way of contacting me—even though I've been reaching out to him the whole time we've been separated. He was able to get a default judgment." The insanity of it all started to overwhelm me. "I've been divorced since June but didn't know it. I am so disgusted. I can't believe he's this crazy. How did I marry him? Oh my gosh!" I was hysterical.

Michael intervened. "Hey—don't start questioning yourself. Don't go down that path. This is what you wanted, right?" he added, focusing on the positives. "You didn't know which way to go before, but now you know for sure."

Michael was right. Now I knew. There were no more questions about the future of my marriage. What was done had been done, and I didn't have to wonder anymore.

"Okay. Thanks. I guess," I said slowly, trying to calm myself. "It's just that I'm so bothered by this. I'm just scared that I was even connected to someone who would do something like this. John is really crazy." I was talking to Michael but to myself as well.

"I know. It's definitely not normal. But now you're free from this situation."

Michael consoled me the best way he could. I was grateful.

"Thank you so much for this. But I suppose I should let you get back to work," I acknowledged, snapping back into reality.

"Are you sure?" he asked, still with concern.

"Yes. I'll be okay."

"Everything will be okay," he said before we exchanged good-byes.

My phone rang again. It was Michelle. I shared the same news, and she expressed the same shock. She was blown away, especially because John had acknowledged the existence of a marriage when he'd spoken to her a couple of months before.

Her advice was similar to Michael's. "God released you," she said.

I paused for a moment to take this in.

"See?" she continued. "You didn't have to do anything, and God revealed everything to you. Now I know it's hard, but continue to trust in God. He is with you, girl!" Michelle was more excited than I was.

"Okay," was the only word I could say.

I called Peter afterward. I'd deleted his number from my phone after the last time we'd spoken, so I had to search through my emails to find his signature with his number. If John thought I was talking to people before, now he would really feel what my talking to people felt like. I hadn't shared many details about what had happened between John and me. But now, I wanted to expose John for who he really was. And I wanted answers.

"Hi, Peter. Sorry for calling you at work."

"It's okay," he said. "I'm just heading to get lunch."

"Well, I just found out today that John got a divorce in June. Did you know that?"

"No, I didn't know anything about it," he said matter-of-factly. "He didn't mention anything about it. But didn't you give John the divorce papers first?"

"Yeah, and you told me to rip them up," I said assertively.

"Oh, right, right. You know I get y'all's situation confused."

Peter's nonchalance was annoying. I didn't stay on the phone much longer to hear his flippantness.

"Okay. Thanks. I just wanted to know. Bye."

I hung up, but for good this time. In that moment, I knew I wanted nothing to do with anyone who could know about such deception and ignore it. Peter should rethink being anyone's best man again.

I was in no condition to concentrate on work. I attended one more meeting for the day, then told my manager I wasn't feeling well and had to go home. I spent the rest of the day on the phone, calling anyone I thought could give me answers.

I spent over two hours talking to Nicole. The first time we'd spoken, I'd mostly listened to her story without saying much about my own, because I was still married—or so I'd thought. There was a lot she didn't know. It was time for her to find out.

I not only told her about the default judgment on the divorce but also the truth about John's livelihood. He was still bringing Nicole to court to reduce his child support payments, claiming he was a meager teacher making $10,000 a year. Nicole didn't know John had a full-time job making over $180,000 a year. She also didn't know that John and I had opened the restaurant.

John's deception didn't just affect Nicole. It also affected Josephine. John had told Josephine we were still married, even when he had already finalized the divorce. It was one of many lies he'd told her over the years. Each time Josephine would visit, John would hide his life from his daughter. He'd ground her for no reason to keep her in her room. To justify his actions toward Josephine to his family and me, he lied some more and painted a horrible picture of Nicole.

Nicole was livid. For thirteen years, John had been bringing Nicole to court for absolutely no reason, causing her to spend over $20,000 in court costs, which basically devoured what little money she did receive for child support. John had provided next to nothing for his child—and he was trying to even provide less. He was the definition of selfishness.

By eight o'clock that night, I was spent. As much as I wanted to get more upset and *do* something, all I could do now was just keep shaking my head. Was John truly a con artist, as he appeared to be? Or was he a misguided boy who never became a man? This was now between John, the legal system, and God. Everything was on the table. Everything would be exposed.

I thought about the positive reminders I had been posting on my standing mirror about trusting in God. I had stayed on the right side of this situation from the beginning, and I would continue to stay on the right side. I focused on the bright future ahead of me.

I decided to send John one last email.

Subject: Hurt . . .

John,
It truly saddens me to see your deceptive actions.
I didn't think you were this kind of person, but you have clearly shown that this is who you are.
I can truly say that everything you have done was unnecessary and only displayed your cowardice.
Hopefully one day you'll see that there is nothing to prove here and be able to be honest with yourself and others so you can be free from denial, lack of self-awareness, and deception—so you can know how to love with your whole heart.
I wish you all the best, John Black.

EPILOGUE

HAPPY

It took almost another year for the divorce to be finalized the proper and right way. It was interesting how efficient and prompt John had been when he'd initiated and obtained a default judgment divorce without my knowledge, yet once I got involved, with lawyers, he was unavailable and unable to respond in a timely fashion.

Having to go through the legal system was very disturbing— even more disturbing than the marriage itself. The whole process was extremely unnecessary. If I had been dealing with a different person, everything could've been resolved outside the courts. But I was dealing with John, whom I now recognized as a completely different person. It was infuriating that I had to get a lawyer in order to hold him accountable for his responsibility and to a basic level of human decency and moral standard.

It forced me to recognize and acknowledge the love that didn't exist and the coldness of the heart that had always been there. John took from me in every way. He took for granted my sacrifices and compromises and gave me deception and wickedness in return. He didn't know how to handle with care.

Over the course of our separation, I believe John was never upset about losing his wife. Rather, he was upset about how he looked in front of other people. It was always about John. His pride caused him to turn his back on reconciliation and made him unable to see the truth about himself so he could do the work for our marriage. Unfortunate.

The whole situation was so crazy that I knew only God could see it through to the end. It had surpassed my level of understanding, and it fell beneath my ability to handle. It was out of my hands and no longer about me. I will never understand John's actions, nor will I try to. But what I do know for sure is what brokenness looks like.

During the many months of the divorce finalization, I took several breaths—deep breaths, ones I could feel intentionally entering and leaving my body. These breaths were of thankfulness. I was okay.

It would be easy to say I never should have married John, but that would devalue the experience and lessons learned. I believed I followed the undercurrent of my life, which led to marrying John. I've taken responsibility for entering the relationship carelessly and being overly trusting with someone I really didn't know. I was naively hopeful, believing it would work out anyway.

The experience taught me to love myself completely. It allowed me to experience my strength and see my faith in action. It gave me the chance to rise to the best version of myself.

I'm thankful for the opportunity to know how it feels to want and then not want a marriage, to know how it feels to be willing to work things out, and to know how it feels to accept what I can't change. I can happily move forward, knowing I came to the table, willing and able, but no one was there.

I decided to stay in Seattle to continue my career and grow my doula business. I feel I've found a second home, a place in which I can plant new roots that will flourish into something beautiful.

I've learned to take better responsibility of my life and know that my life is not up for negotiation—with anyone. I sacrificed a lot of myself for John and for the marriage. That's something I can't regret but only learn from. My heart was and still remains pure, and I would never want to change that.

I thought I'd never want to be in another relationship, but each day gets better. I'm reminded of what I didn't experience: love. I'm reminded of what is still out there to experience: love.

I found my own strength. It is no longer something I expect someone else to recognize and offer back to me as a compliment. Rather, it's something I know for sure on my own. My strength is unshakeable. I'm standing firm on both my feet.

Today, I dance in my dress as it blows in the direction of the wind. My head tilts back, and my arms stretch from sea to sea. I take a deep inhale. Smile and exhale.

Thank you.

Trust in the LORD with all thine heart; and lean not unto thine own understanding. In all thy ways acknowledge him, and he shall direct thy paths.

—PROVERBS 3: 5-6

QUESTIONS AND TOPICS FOR DISCUSSION

1. Social pressure to be married plays a huge role throughout the novel. For Justyne, her impatience for a proposal ultimately put her in a difficult situation that may have turned out differently if she had simply waited. Discuss the social ideas of marriage, its evolution, and how it impacts women today.

2. We see Justyne recognize her faith in God and ask for His guidance to endure a less-than-ideal situation. How does Justyne's faith help and not help in moments throughout her relationship journey?

3. Discuss the role of faith in the novel. How does faith impact the decisions made? Consider the concept of blind faith and the role it played in the novel.

4. We learn about the peace Justyne made with the marriage and how she surrendered it to God. Discuss Justyne's character development from the time when she first gave John the divorce papers to the time when she was willing to work together toward a civilized resolution. How was Justyne able to get to a neutral place? How does it shed light on how we view difficult moments, especially in relationships?

5. John's character takes many different turns throughout the novel. Discuss John's character transitions through his interactions with Justyne. What do you think John was feeling and thinking in those moments? Discuss how those moments impacted the relationship.

6. We see John's family play an important role in the demise of John and Justyne's relationship. Traditionally, extended family does play an important role in a marriage. However, John's close family relationships appear to impact the progression of his marriage. Discuss the role of extended family in marriage today. What was Justyne's reaction toward John's family?

7. Compare the proposals Justyne received from Michael and John. Discuss the differences and similarities. How do you feel Justyne felt about the proposals?

8. Perhaps one of the saddest moments in the novel is Justyne's early labor and ultimate loss of her and John's son. What do you think led to this loss? How do you think it impacted the relationship and marriage?

9. Discuss the character of Michael Turner. What do you make of his relationship with Justyne?

10. Technology was a major form of communication in Justyne and John's relationship. What impact did communicating via email and text have on their relationship? Discuss the role technology plays in communications within relationships today.

11. Many things about John are revealed to Justyne when they are separated. Justyne discovers the state of John's finances during the marriage as well as the true nature of his relationship with his ex-wife, Nicole. Discuss how these important factors were kept hidden.

12. Perhaps the most surprising revelation in the novel is when Justyne finds out she was already divorced. Discuss Justyne's reaction as well as your personal reaction as a reader. What thoughts about John surfaced?

13. How do you personally relate to Justyne's journey from eagerness, endurance, and sadness to love? What love did she discover at the end?

14. The end of the novel provides an eloquent depiction of strength that is quite inspiring. Justyne makes the claim that her life is "not up for negotiation—with anyone." Discuss the meaning and significance of this claim. Why do you think Justyne mentioned she learned to take better responsibility for her life? Discuss moments in the novel where this was not the case.

15. Consider the silent role Justyne's mother played in her relationships. Discuss the influences that may have impacted Justyne's decisions.

16. Discuss Justyne's choice to remain in Seattle. Do you think Justyne should have returned to Belleville? What would you have done?